TEACHING Tricky Bits

SCIENCE

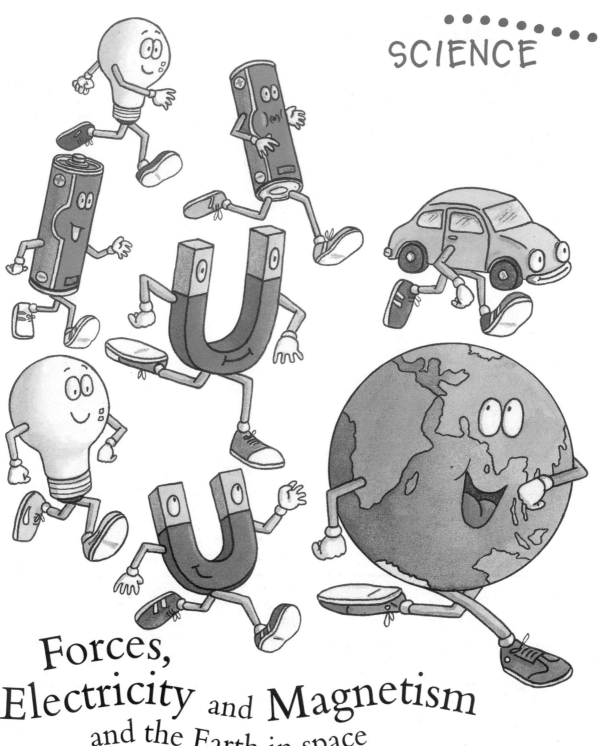

Forces, Electricity and Magnetism
and the Earth in space

John Stringer

Published by
Hopscotch Educational Publishing Ltd,
29 Waterloo Place,
Leamington Spa CV32 5LA
Tel: 01926 744227

© 2001 Hopscotch Educational Publishing

Written by John Stringer
Series design by Blade Communications
Illustrated by Bernard Connors
Printed by Clintplan, Southam

ISBN 1-902239-69-5

Contents

About the series

Teaching the Tricky Bits arose out of a frustrated teacher's cry for help when one of the children in her class said 'But why do we need blood?' She sort-of knew the answer but couldn't quite explain it so that the child could understand.

So the concept of a series of books that would inform teachers about the different science topics in the National Curriculum began to be developed.

But soon we realised that often information on science tends to be dry and can only be taken in in bite-sized pieces for fear of falling asleep. So we need a series of books that would keep teachers informed and awake!

This is what we have achieved. This book and the other three in the series all contain vital, useful and fascinating information written by John Stringer, a member of the primary committee of the Association for Science Education and well-known author of science materials. But just as important as the information John has supplied

is the approach he has taken with his writing – it's fun to read! There are amusing scenarios and anecdotes. You really won't fall asleep!

Then we realised that it's all well and good having all this information and rolling about in the aisles laughing, but what are you going to do with it? Or, more importantly, what are the children going to do with your new-found knowledge?

So, John has provided relevant activities for each chapter, starting with what could be done at level 1 and going all the way to level 5.

This makes these books ideal for every teacher. You can allocate activities according to ability. You can still use the book if you find yourself teaching a different age group.

We hope you enjoy reading and using this book as much as we have enjoyed putting it together!

Other titles in the series are:

The Human Body

ISBN 1 902239 68 7

Materials

ISBN 1 902239 70 9

Plants and animals

ISBN 1 902239 69 5

Introduction

So what are forces?

Forces are behind everything that is happening around us. Forces make things happen.

You probably think the subject is difficult. You are quite right to fear getting too deeply into it because when you do, you will have to suspend your disbelief and your trust in common sense. Forces just don't behave as we would expect them to. Teaching forces is not easy!

Take these examples. Which of them would you think are true?

1 Two balls the same size dropped together from the top of the Leaning Tower of Pisa will both hit the ground at the same moment, even if one is a foam ball and the other is made from lead.

2 A bullet fired horizontally across a field from a gun, and an identical bullet dropped at the same moment from the barrel, will both hit the ground simultaneously.

3 When you sit on a table, it pushes back at you with an equal and opposite force.

4 There are two forces acting on a kicked football once it is in the air – the drag of the air and the downward pull of gravity.

5 The force of gravity is pulling you downward – but you are also pulling the Earth towards you with your own force of gravity.

True or false?

That's right – all of them are true.

Well, almost. Here's why.

Question 1

This is only true if the Leaning Tower of Pisa is – just for the moment – in a vacuum. If you have tried this at school, climbing to the top of the caretaker's ladder with a foam ball and a medicine ball, you will have found that the medicine ball does indeed hit the ground first – just. The air friction effects on each are different.

What's going on here? Well, the moment you let go of them, they both accelerate away from rest. The heavier the object, the harder it is to accelerate. (Which would you rather bump start, a Mini or a lorry?) So the heavy ball is actually harder to start – even to start falling. (I warned you this was difficult.) But the mass of the heavy ball being greater than that of the light one, it gets more of a tug from gravity. These two differences just about balance each other out, so away go both balls at about the same rate – and if the air doesn't intervene, both hit the ground together.

Got that? Galileo certainly did – although his was just a thought experiment. He never climbed the Tower of Pisa with a cannon ball to put his theory to the test. That had to wait nearly four hundred years until the first man on the Moon, Neil Armstrong, dropped a hammer and a feather together in perfect, air-free conditions – and they both hit the ground together.

Question 2

The same answer applies to the bullets from the gun. Both bullets are feeling the effects of the two forces – air friction and gravity. Both are being pulled down. Both hit the ground at the same moment. For more on this unlikely event read the answer to question 4!

Question 3

Sit on a flexible horizontal bar from the PE apparatus. It bends, doesn't it? You can almost see it pushing back at you, as if it were a sling and you were the stone. It's possible to believe that, with a really springy bar, you could jump on it and it would bounce you upwards – a bit like a diving-board. So why can't you handle the idea that the table pushes back at you, too? The only real difference is that the table is more rigid – which is just as well, or dinner plates would all slide to the dip in the middle.

Question 4

This topic was a hot issue after it turned up in a SAT paper a few years ago. We can all accept that the flying football was subject to gravity; if it wasn't it would go humming off into outer space, never to be seen again. But countless children – and teachers too – were confused about the second force. Surely the second force on the airborne football comes from the kicker's foot. Well, not once it's left your toe, sunshine. After that it's on its own.

My father once kicked a football back to a gang of children playing in the park. Unfortunately, his football skills were not a patch on his tennis skills, and the ball flew into a nearby garden. Being a gentleman, my father went round and knocked on the door and asked for his ball back.

What my father learned – and we all know, really – is that once the ball has left our foot we have no control over it. It can fly where it likes – or rather, where you first directed it. The only force acting on it then (apart from gravity) is the slowing down friction force of the air. See? Easy, really.

Question 5

We can all accept that the Earth pulls us down with a force we call gravity. Without it, we would be in trouble. But this isn't the only force in the frame. You have a force of gravity too. It's pretty small compared with that of the Earth, but your pull on the Earth is equivalent to the force the Earth exerts on you, allowing for the slight difference in size between you and a planet.

So that means that no matter how small you are, you make a tiny difference – just by being there.

Ready for more?

If you've read this far, you must be game for the whole story of forces. It's surprising, implausible and exciting. You certainly shouldn't worry about it. The chances that Newton's third law of motion will turn up during a plasticine activity with Year 2 are slight. But once you've read this book, at least you will have the confidence of knowing what's behind all this forces stuff. And if you feel comfortable with your knowledge, you will teach with more confidence.

Welcome to tricky forces!

Fascinating facts

- Golf balls have dimples to reduce the air friction on their surface, so that the same force will carry them further.

- Water would run clockwise out of a perfectly symmetrical bathtub in the Northern Hemisphere, and anticlockwise in the Southern Hemisphere. This is due to the spin of the Earth – not gravity.

- Water on the equator (and in that perfect bath!) would run straight down.

Pushes and pulls

Forces are pushes and pulls. You can't escape forces – they are around you all the time.

Pushing and pulling

When you are cycling, you need to push on the pedals to move forward. The ground is pulling on your tyres to slow you down. The air is pushing in your face. If you stop pedalling, the ground and the air will slow you down until you come to a stop, but their forces keep working.

Clip a trailer on the back of the bike. Now you are pulling. Your force on the trailer is a pulling force. You push the pedals; the bike pulls the trailer! Stop cycling and try sitting still. Surely no forces are acting now? In fact, the force of gravity is pulling down on you. And the ground is pushing back.

The ground? Pushing? Yes – it has to. If the ground didn't push back, you would fall to the middle of the Earth. So the ground pushes on your bike, and your bike pushes on you. Good thing, too. You don't want to disappear into the Earth!

Moving or keeping still, forces are acting on you all the time!

Forces are pushes and pulls. You can model a force in action. Blow up a long balloon and close the end with a clothes-peg. Tape a drinking straw to the long balloon, and slip some fishing-line through it. Tie the ends of the fishing-line to the backs of two chairs. When you open the clothes-peg, the balloon will travel along the line. It is being pushed by the force of the escaping air.
You can measure forces using the units named after Isaac Newton. You need a force meter. You can use it to pull some light objects along. How many newtons does it take? You can use it to lift some small objects. How great is the pull of gravity on them?

Forces all around

When you sit on a chair, you are pushing on the chair and it is pushing back at you. When you put a book on a table, the book pushes on the table and the table pushes back on the book.

You don't believe it? Try this. Take a long piece of wood – a metre rule is perfect – and a book. Rest one end of the rule on the table and hold the other in your hand. Now balance a book carefully in the middle of the rule. See it bend? You can see how the book pushes down on the ruler – and how the bendy rule pushes back. If the rule didn't push back, the book would continue to push down until the rule snapped.

Shorten the rule by holding it further in. Put the book on the middle again. See how the rule bends? Keep on shortening the rule and putting the book on it. Eventually you can't see the rule bending any more. But it is still pushing back on the book. Put the book on the table. The table is pushing back at the book.

Faster and slower

You are using forces when you change speed. Hop on a scooter. First, you want to accelerate. Push off with your foot. The ground is pushing back at you and you're away! Want to go faster? It's no good just thinking about it. A bit of force is needed. Foot down, push again, and again. That's better. Now you are really rolling.

Lamppost ahead. Time to slow down. Push your foot to the ground. Slowing ... whoops! Bit of a mistake there. The lamppost is still coming up. Brakes on. Put foot down and push backwards. Too late. Contact. Unfortunately, the lamppost pushed back just as hard as you pushed on it. It certainly stopped you. Unfortunately, it also changed the shape of your nose!

Try rolling a film canister down a slope. Keep the slope at the same angle all the time. How can you speed up the movement of the canister? How can you slow it down? Add modelling clay to the inside of the canister.

- What difference does it make to its speed?
- What difference does it make to how far it rolls?

With modelling clay in the canister, it will roll faster and farther. The energy you expend lifting the heavier canister to the top of the ramp has to turn up somewhere, and it appears in the behaviour of the canister. Try putting loose sand or sugar in the canister, and something interesting happens. It doesn't roll nearly so far. Why should this be? The sand is rubbing against the inside of the canister and against itself, and this frictional force expends the energy. This is the action of friction (see Chapter 4).

Changing direction

You can't change direction without a force. It might be the push and pull you give to the scooter handlebars. It might be the push and pull you give to a steering wheel. It might be the twisting force you give to your leg as you jump sideways to catch a ball. (You can see the results of that force if you look at the soles of your trainers. Old trainers get a well-worn jumping-off spot.)

Isaac Newton, the great scientist, stated this as a law in 1687. He said that every object would remain still, or carry on moving in the same direction at a steady speed, unless forces acted on it. This is called Newton's first law of motion.

Fascinating facts

- The slowest mammal in the world is the three-toed sloth from South America. When it is really in a hurry, it can walk at two and a half metres a minute. However slow it is, it still needs some force to push it along.

- The fastest car from 0–96 kph is a Ford RS2000 Evolution. One took just over three seconds to reach this speed from standstill in 1994. To go that fast, it had to do an awful lot of pushing.

It doesn't matter whether it is speeding up, slowing down or changing direction, you need forces for change! Forces make things change direction. Try bouncing a ball. It changes direction when it hits the ground or the wall. But the new direction can be predicted. Try rolling a ball against the wall and seeing which way it bounces off. What do you notice? You can predict the angle – especially if you are a good snooker player!

Machines

You can modify the effects of forces – change their direction or multiply them! Something that can multiply forces is called a machine. The word 'machine' is used to cover a great many things, from steam engines to computers. But to a physicist, there are five classic machines. These are the lever, the wheel, the ramp, the screw and the pulley. The screw and the ramp are closely related. The screw is really a ramp, wound round itself.

The ramp and the screw

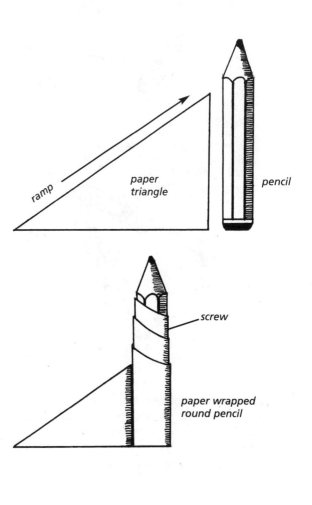

Levers

A machine is a device that makes work easier, and the simplest example is the lever. Levers make it easier to open tins, to pull nails and to lift weights. We even use a couple of levers every time we open the door.

Levers have three things in common:

- a place to apply a bit of effort
- a turning point or fulcrum
- a place where the work is done.

Normally, the end where we apply the effort is longer than the end where the work is done. As a result of moving this extra distance, we are able to apply more effort at the business end.

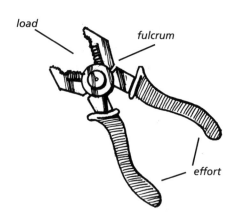

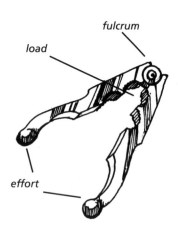

Take opening a door. The handle is at the opposite side to the hinge. If you wonder why, try getting up now and closing the door three times. The first time, close it by pushing at the handle side. The second time, try pushing in the middle of the door. The third time, push at the hinge side. See how the door is a lever and how using the lever makes closing the door very much easier?

Wheels

Another classic machine is the wheel. This works as if the spokes were levers, turning around the central axle. Once again, the wheel makes moving loads a lot easier than carrying them – or even rolling them along.

Pulleys

A simple pulley is a good way of lifting a heavy weight because our bodies are made so that we can pull down more easily than we can lift up. We pull down through the same distance as the load moves upward.

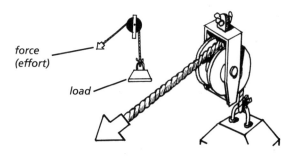

Two pulley wheels introduce the possibility of lifting a load more easily – a so-called mechanical advantage. You pull the rope through twice the distance that the load travels, but you only pull half the 'weight'.

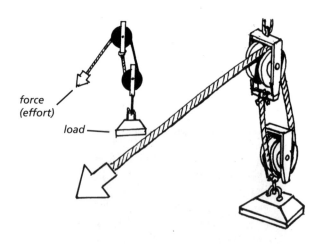

Look for examples of pulleys around you. There are pulleys in many domestic appliances – they turn the brushes of a vacuum cleaner and the turntable of a microwave oven. Most are hidden, not least because they could catch fingers if they were accessible. Lifting a car bonnet reveals a number of pulleys – turning the generator or alternator, turning camshafts, or the pumps for power steering or air-conditioning.

The block and tackle uses a compact set of pulleys to lift large loads with very little force. The rope is wound round a double set of pulleys. The upper set is connected to a strong support; the bottom set to the load. Pulling the rope shortens all the ropes between the two sets of pulleys, drawing them closer together. The more pulleys in the set, the greater the magnification of the effort. A set of eight pulley wheels reduces the force needed – the effort – eight times, less a bit of loss through friction. So a mechanic can lift a car engine unaided, even if it weighs more than they do. You will see a block and tackle at the end of crane booms or arms; they greatly increase the force of the crane's engine in lifting a load.

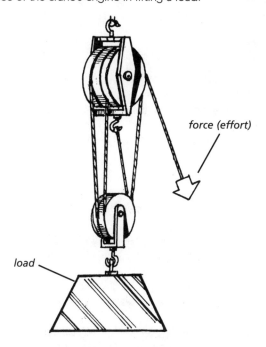

force (effort)

load

How do we show forces?

We show forces in pictures by drawing arrows. Always draw the arrow in the same direction as the force. Use longer arrows for bigger forces, shorter arrows for smaller forces. The arrows always show the direction of the force but they don't show where the force is working. So a push force and a pull force look alike. The longer the arrow, the stronger the force.

Blowing and squirting

There are lots of forces involved with balloons and pumps. These include simple pneumatics (blowing air) and hydraulics (squirting water). You find them when using:

- a balloon pump to inflate balloons
- straws to play blow football
- an empty detergent bottle to blow down targets
- a detergent bottle to blow up balloons
- detergent bottles to make a jet
- a hose or garden spray.

Fascinating facts

- Scientists have always dreamed of making a perpetual motion machine, one that would go on working for ever. All machines need energy to keep working.

- The first known pulleys were simple cranes invented around 2,000BC. Pulleys using several wheels were used some 1,500 years later. The crane, invented by the Greek scientist Archimedes (c287-212BC), was reputed to be able to lift a ship out of the water, using compound pulley wheels.

What is happening? You are transferring forces, often over a distance. When you pump up a balloon, the energy you expend is stored in the compressed air of the inflated balloon and in the stretch of the balloon skin. Let the neck go and all that energy (and all the compressed air!) shoot the balloon into the air. Some of the energy may also be transferred to the production of a long and amusing sound.

Water is not compressible like air. If you squeeze a detergent bottle of water, it will not squash. Instead, the water is ejected from the end, with the force you have given it. Anything light in the way will get knocked over. This is hydraulic force. You use the same transfer of force when you hit the brake pedal of your car – squeezing the brake discs with high friction pads.

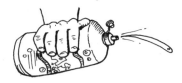

Or, even simpler, you use hydraulics every time you clean your teeth. As you squeeze the toothpaste – ideally from the end! – the paste appears at the nozzle. The force you applied to the closed end was transferred by the paste to the open end of the tube.

Stretch and squeeze

This is another great area for children to experience through gymnastics. They can stretch and squeeze, feeling the forces acting on their own bodies. They can try classroom activities, including:

- stretching elastic bands (care and control are needed, and eye protection should be worn if there is any danger of the bands snapping)
- stretching light springs (exercise great care)
- compressing springs (you can also try making paper concertinas, which compress and extend easily).

These activities give children experience of the way in which forces can be stored; in a stretched elastic band, for example – waiting for release. When you wind a clock, you store forces in the wound spring ready for slow release over the next week or so. When you store them in a stretched elastic band, you are ready to release them – very suddenly – as you flick a paper pellet towards an innocent victim.

Two special forces

There are two special forces. They are also invisible. But they don't need to touch an object. They can act on an object without touching it.

1 Magnetism

Magnets exert forces. The forces act on magnetic materials. Some metals, like iron and steel, are magnetic but not all metals are magnetic. Magnetic metals can be attracted over a distance. Magnets can repel other magnets, too. They can push other magnets over a distance (see Chapter 2).

2 Gravity

Gravity works over a distance, too. All objects have gravity. But for those of us on the Earth, the gravity pull of the Earth is the nearest and strongest by far. The Earth's gravity holds us on the Earth. If you drop something, it will always fall downward. The Earth's gravity pulls it down.

Remember

- In science, a force is a push or a pull, or a special sort of pull called a twist.

- Forces can speed things up. If you push someone in a go-kart, you speed them up.

- Forces can slow things down. If you pull back on a runaway car, you slow it down (although it might not seem like it's slowing if you are on your own!).

- Forces can make things change direction. If you are on rollerblades, you can push yourself in a different direction. If you are on a bike, you can pull the handlebars to change direction. If a snooker ball bounces, the cushion it bounces off gives it a new direction. The cushion applies a force; the snooker ball changes direction.

Fascinating facts

- Stefan Topurov is a strong guy. He overcame the force of gravity in 1983 when he was 19. He lifted three times the weight of his own body – 180kg.

Activities

Level One

Encourage the children to note as many of the forces around them as they can. Ask them to group the forces they see as pushes and pulls.

Challenge the children to become force detectives. Use sticky notes or small cards with sticky tack on them to label things round the classroom – 'We push this'; 'We pull this'. Beware of things that it would be dangerous to push or pull.

Level Two

Give the children a selection of objects. Ask them to explore and record the way things squash and stretch.

Ball games and all activities involving movement are an opportunity to explore how forces make things change shape or direction. Balls bounce, changing direction. Children push off from walls or the floor, using the force to propel themselves forward. Encourage the children to explore how the brakes and steering of a bike use the forces they apply to change their direction of movement. They can explore the changes in shape that result from the application of pushes and pulls to modelling clay.

Level Three

The children can try stretching springs and elastic bands. A circle of paper, cut into a spiral, makes a spring that can be investigated easily. Tape one end of the spiral to the desk edge. Hang the other end over the edge and add paper-clips, one by one. Children can record the stretch of the paper spring with increased weight.

Level Four

Invite the children to illustrate forces using arrows for the direction and size. For example, they could explore the forces in action in a tug-of-war or a rugby football scrum. Both may be unmoving, but nobody could say that there were no forces involved! Ask the children to draw arrows on pictures of these to show the forces involved and their direction and strength. Larger arrows represent larger forces. Ask them to draw the forces at work when a book is placed on a table or when a child sits in a chair.

Level Five

Ask the children to explain the effects of forces using simple models. For example, ask them to explain how they change direction or speed when riding a bike or scooter.

Ask the children to describe a short journey by micro-scooter. They set off, speed and slow, turn a corner and stop. Ask them to explain the forces involved if they were to bump into another rider or a wall!

Is magnetism magic?

Magnets are magical and mysterious – a sure winner with children. They are also excellent subjects for investigations. All you need are a few well-chosen questions.

The mysterious force

Magnetism has been known about for thousands of years. Around 2,300 years ago, the Chinese 'Book of the Devil Valley Master' first mentioned a mysterious rock, called lodestone, that was naturally magnetic. When hung from a string, it turned to face north-south. For this reason, the Chinese called it a 'south-pointer'.

But it was a scientist in the Middle Ages, Petrus Peregrinus, who first described experimenting with the curious behaviour of magnets. This made him one of the first true scientists.

Are all metals magnetic?

Yes and no. In fact, everything is magnetic, but the magnetic pull on most objects – including you – is very slight. It would take a very powerful magnet indeed to attract you. Iron, iron alloys (like steel), cobalt, cadmium and nickel are very magnetic. But other metals are attracted only by hugely powerful magnets. This means that it is, for example, very easy to separate steel and aluminium cans. Steel cans are attracted to a magnet, and aluminium cans are not.

Small changes to metals can make them magnetic or non-magnetic. Steel, an alloy of iron made with a tiny amount of carbon and other chemicals, is magnetic. Stainless steel, which has a tiny amount of chromium in it too, is not magnetic. As a result, stainless steel can be separated from ordinary steel in a scrapyard, using a magnet.

You can sort a collection of drinks cans into steel and aluminium, using a magnet. (Test the ends as well as the sides of the cans – sometimes the ends of an aluminium can are made of steel.) Cans are sometimes called 'tins' because the steel can is covered with a thin layer of tin. But the metal called tin is not magnetic – it is the steel inside the can that sticks to the magnet.

How is a magnet made?

A material like iron is made up of countless tiny bits, all of them magnets. Usually, these little bits are facing randomly, like people crowded into a room. When the iron is made magnetic, all the magnetic bits face the same way. It's as if you open a window at one end of the room, and everyone turns to face it.

You can see that those people in front of the window, and those near the back wall, have nobody in front of or behind them. The magnetic bits at the ends of a magnet have no bits in front of or behind them. They are the poles of the magnet – the points of greatest magnetic force.

Fascinating facts

- A letter written in 1269 by the scientist calling himself Peter the Pilgrim has the first mention of the poles of a magnet.

- The poles of the Earth can change. Magnetic lines of rocks laid down long ago show that once the North Pole was the South Pole; and the South Pole, the North.

This might be easier to understand from the point of view of a magnetic particle.

It's very crowded in this bar of metal. There are lots of other particles – just like me – all packed in here. We're all vibrating gently, but as we are not particles in a liquid, we can't move about. If we were particles in a gas, we could go where we liked!

No, we're stuck here, facing in every direction, and scarcely able to move. That particle there is facing me; that one is looking away. Those over there are sideways on.

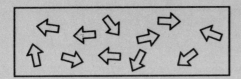

But what's that? I can feel a force pulling at me. Someone has brought a magnet close to us. We're all turning towards the magnet. Now I'm facing the magnet, and so are all the other particles. All I can see in front of me is backs. Behind me, all the particles are facing my back. I'm locked in this position by the tiny magnetic force I've got. So is everybody else. All our magnetic forces are facing the same way. So those particles at the ends have nothing in front of them or behind them. They are free to grab anything magnetic passing by because we're all pulling together. They're our poles. Gosh, we're a magnet!

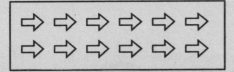

But heat a magnet, give it a good bashing, or let little Jimmy drop it on the classroom floor a few times, and all the magnetic bits will end up facing randomly again. Your magnet is weakened or destroyed. It's a good idea to put your magnets away with 'keepers'. These bridge the ends or poles of a pair of magnets and ensure that the magnetic force is circled and enclosed. Your magnets will last a lot longer if you do this!

The Earth is a magnet

Four hundred years ago, a scientist named William Gilbert made a dramatic suggestion. He had looked at the way magnets turned to face north-south. This would happen, he argued, if the Earth itself were a huge magnet.

He was right. Around every magnet there is an area, a 'field', where the invisible force of magnetism is operating. The Earth has its own magnetic field. It has poles, just like any other magnet, which are not quite in the same places as the true north and south of the Earth.

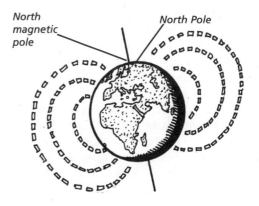

North magnetic pole   *North Pole*

Compasses have a magnetic needle in them that is free to swing around. One pole of this magnet – the 'north-seeking' pole – turns to face north. Wherever you are on Earth, you can know the compass direction with a free-turning magnet.

What is a force field?

We all have a vague understanding of force fields from programmes like 'Star Trek'. They act without the space ships touching. We imagine them as invisible barriers. Likewise, magnets can push and pull things without touching them. They can do this because there is a force field around each magnet. In this invisible field, the magnet can not only repel some metal objects and other magnets, but also attract them. A piece of magnetic metal in the force field of a magnet is drawn to it. There is no escape. The door of a fridge works like this. A long magnet, all along the edge of the fridge, grabs for the metal door as soon as it comes close and sucks it shut.

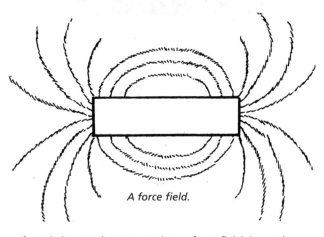

A force field.

If you bring another magnet into a force field, it may be attracted and trapped. But it may be repelled, so that you have to push hard to get the magnets to touch each other.

Some trains ride on a magnetic force field. Because they don't touch the track and so are free of the track's friction, they can travel very fast.The Maglev train between the station and terminal at Birmingham Airport was one of the first of these trains. Both train and rail created a magnetic field. These opposing fields kept the two apart, so that there was no friction between the train and the rails – and no wheels! The train was floating just 1.5cm above the track, and it was pulled along by electromagnets alongside the track that switched on, one by one, passing the train from one to another as it moved along the track. The Maglev could carry over two thousand passengers an hour at 40km per hour. Today in Japan high-speed frictionless Maglev trains can travel at up to 500km per hour.

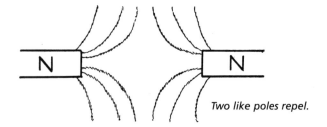

Two like poles repel.

If different poles of two magnets are brought together – north to south, or south to north – they attract each other. But if the same poles are brought together – north to north or south to south – they repel. You know that a metal bar is a magnet when it is repelled by another magnet. If it were just a magnetic metal bar, and not a magnet, it could be attracted, but not repelled. Attraction is not a test of a magnet.

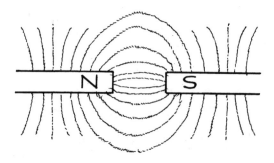

Two unlike poles attract.

How can you find the force field?

You can find the force field by putting a bar-magnet in the centre of a piece of paper. Slide a compass close to it. Watch how the compass needle moves. Draw round the compass and lift it away. Now draw the way the needle was facing on the circle outline. Put the compass on a different area of the paper and draw the needle again. Repeat this a number of times. Notice which way the needles are facing. These directions are the magnet's lines of force. Together, these lines make up the force field. Ask Luke Skywalker or Darth Vader!

Can a magnet work through things?

A magnetic field can work right through other objects. You can make something magnetic move on a table top by attracting it with a magnet underneath the table. You can make it stick to the bottom of the table by putting a magnet on the table top. The magnetic field works through the table.

The magnetic field can work through you, too. Magnetic resonance imaging (MRI) uses powerful magnets to build up a picture of the inside of a human body. The magnetic field passes though your body so that doctors can see inside you without cutting you open. An MRI scanner works because of the different ways that tissues of the body respond to a magnetic field. Using this technique, it is possible to make detailed three-dimensional pictures of the inside of a patient, including the soft organs and tissues, and without using harmful radiation.

Different shapes and sizes

Magnets come as:

- bar-magnets
- horseshoe magnets
- ring magnets, which can be made to float
- magnetic play kits (these have a magnetic base, and lots of shiny steel pieces that can be made into models)
- flexible magnetic sheet and string
- magnetic compasses.

Bar-magnets are straight, with a pole at each end – the north and south poles. Horseshoe magnets are curved so that both the poles can pull together on a metal bar. Some magnets are round with a hole in them like a mint sweet. The poles are on the faces of the magnets. There are also magnetic marbles. These are spherical, but they contain a tiny bar-magnet. One side of the marble is the north pole, and the other is the south pole.

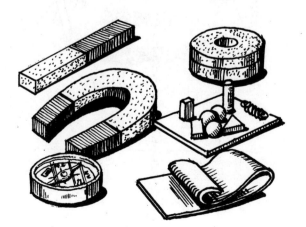

Some magnets come in tapes, strips and strings. You can bend them and cut them with scissors. There are 'rubber' magnets – magnetic strips made from tiny magnets in ribbons of rubber. There are magnetic tapes made from plastic. Look for the brown strip on the back of many identification cards. These are magnetic, too. This strip of magnetic tape identifies bank and club membership cards to cash machines and locks. The numbers on the bottom of a cheque are in magnetic ink.

For use in the classroom, you can also buy a set of labelled metals. The best look like coins, and come on a string, which helps keep them together. They will help the children discover that not all metals are magnetic. You can buy iron filings for use with magnets. Buy them sealed in plastic bubbles because when they are loose they quickly get stuck to magnets and are potentially dangerous as they could be rubbed into children's eyes.

Can a magnet make electricity?

Electricity plus magnetism produces movement. And movement plus magnetism will produce electricity. If electricity flows through a wire, it produces magnetism and can move a magnet. And the reverse is true. If you move a magnet near a wire, then you generate electricity. You are doing just this if you have a dynamo on your bike. As you cycle along, you are providing the movement, and the moving magnets in the dynamo generate electricity.

This was Michael Faraday's shattering discovery. Without this form of electricity generation, only batteries would provide our electricity. His invention changed the world. Electricity generators contain magnets. When you make the magnets move using a steam turbine, moving water or the power of the wind, you generate electricity.

How are magnetism and static electricity different?

Static electricity (see Chapter 6) can be made when two surfaces are rubbed together. You make static electricity when you rub a balloon with a jumper. Magnetism and static electricity are both forces that can work at a distance. A magnet can attract a piece of steel to it and repel another magnet; a charged balloon can attract or repel another balloon. But magnetism is safe. Huge magnets can be used to scan your body in hospital. Static electricity can be very powerful, and very dangerous. Lightning is a huge explosion of static electricity. It is jumping to Earth, with a rumble of thunder. And it could jump through a piece of string – or through you.

Electromagnets

The connection between electricity and magnetism was discovered in a classroom. In 1820, Hans Christian Oersted was teaching about electricity when he brought a magnetic compass close to the wire. To his amazement, the compass needle moved suddenly to line up with the wire. He realised that the electricity through the wire was making its own magnetic field.

There is a magnetic field around any wire that carries an electric current. Electromagnets have this wire coiled around a metal coil. Electromagnets are magnets that can be switched on and off. When they are off, they are just iron bars inside a coil of insulated wire. When they are switched on, they become powerful magnets that can lift scrap metal, ring doorbells, and pull a steel splinter from your eye.

When the electric current is switched on, the coiled wire creates a magnetic field. When the electric current is turned off, the magnetism is reduced. An iron core will stop being an electromagnet altogether. But a steel core becomes slightly magnetic. Each time you switch on the electromagnet, the steel becomes more and more magnetic.

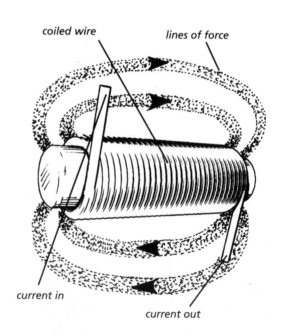

coiled wire   lines of force

current in

current out

Fascinating facts

- The first electromagnet was made by an English scientist called William Sturgeon in 1825. It could lift a few pins. Modern electromagnets can lift whole cars. Some are so powerful they affect metals, like copper, which are not usually magnetic.

This is how permanent magnets are made – by using an electric coil. A metal bar is put inside a strong coil. The electricity is switched on, and the metal bar becomes magnetised. The stronger the current, and the longer the bar is in the coil, the stronger the magnet. You can use a coil like this to 'repair' weak magnets, too.

You can make your own electromagnet. Wind a thin insulated wire round a large nail. Make the winding even, like thread on a cotton reel. Touch the two ends of the wire to a battery.

DO NOT hold the wires to the battery for too long. You are making a 'short circuit' and the battery will run down very quickly. The wires might get hot, too! Use your electromagnet to pick up pins and paper-clips. What happens when you take the wires away from the battery?

There are hundreds of electromagnets around you. They are in the motors that work gadgets in your kitchen, in the windows and wipers of cars and in many electric locks and switches.

Do we still need magnets?

More than ever! We use magnets in many amazing ways. A minidisc recorder, for example, will fit in the palm of your hand, and weighs around 100g. But a 65mm minidisc can hold as much stereo sound as a CD – that's around 80 minutes of music. The sound is recorded on a special magnetic layer on the disc. The music can only be recorded when the disc is heated with a laser.

New 'smart' cards don't need to be swiped to pay for something or to let you through a gate. The card sends out a weak magnetic signal. If you have the card in your pocket, you just need to walk near a special aerial and the cashpoint will know you are there, or the gate will open to let you through. Cards like these will let you on the bus or onto a station platform, and take the money for the fare from your bank.

Fascinating facts

● Your favourite music and television programmes can be stored magnetically. Sound and video tapes are plastic ribbons with a magnetic coat. Information is recorded on the tapes as magnetic fields. Stroke them with a magnet and all this information (which includes the sound and pictures) will be lost forever.

Activities

Level One

Let the children explore magnets to find out that they pick up some things, but not others. Give them a range of everyday objects, including some that are clearly not magnetic and some that are. Include some metal objects that are not magnetic. They can also explore this by testing some objects around the room. Door handles and taps, although metal, may not be magnetic. Ask the children to record their findings by grouping the names of the objects or pictures of them.

Warn the children not to test watches, which can be permanently damaged by a magnet, and never to test electrical switches and sockets.

Level Two

Challenge the children to discover which metal objects are made from and so which metals are magnetic. Ask them to record their results in a two-column table.

You could use a test set of marked metals for this investigation. You can obtain sets of labelled metal discs from science suppliers, and these will help children to identify the metals they are testing. Note that we often use the names of metals incorrectly. So 'tins' for example may be made of steel or aluminium. Some steel cans are coated in tin.

Level Three

Show the children how to make their own magnets. Take a small piece of iron or steel (a straightened paper-clip is ideal). Then stroke it, end to end, with a magnet, always using the same end and stroking in the same direction.

Then show the children how to make their own compasses. Take a sewing needle, a cork and a bowl of water. Stroke the needle from one end to the other, using one pole of the magnet. Always use the same pole and stroke in the same direction. Try fifty strokes. Then put the needle on a cork floating in a bowl of water. It should turn to face north-south. Check with a magnetic compass.

Level Four

Invite the children to find out how many ways there are of finding the stronger of two magnets. They might see which can lift more paper-clips, or which lifts the heavier object. They could see which holds the longer chain of touching paper-clips. Alternatively, they might investigate which can move a paper-clip through the larger number of pages.

Ask the children to investigate where the magnetism is in a magnet. They could try hanging chains of paper-clips from the ends and from the middle of a magnet. The magnetism is in the poles – the ends. The longer chains can be hung there.

Level Five

Encourage the children to record the force field around a magnet – either by placing small compasses close to the magnet and recording the direction of the compass needle at each point (joining these records gives an idea of the force fields) or by using iron filings sealed inside a plastic bubble for safety.

As a demonstration, you could put a magnet on the table, cover it with a sheet of paper, and sprinkle iron filings on the paper. They will line up to show the field of force. Sandwich your pattern with a wet paper towel, leave it for a few days, and you will have a permanent record in rust.

Note that children should not be allowed to handle loose filings because of the slight danger of rubbing them in their eyes.

What's pulling on us all?

The apple tree

We all dream that we could be as clever as the great scientist, Sir Isaac Newton. 'If only an apple fell on my head,' we think, 'it would rattle my brain. I could have some brilliant ideas like him.'

Bad news. The apple never fell on Newton's head. Thousands of artists have drawn the apple conking poor old Isaac, and a light bulb lighting up. Idea! Now I can explain gravity.

Sadly, it wasn't like that. As Newton explained to a friend, he was walking in an orchard, puzzling over the problem of gravity, when an apple fell. 'Why does that apple fall downwards?', he thought. 'Why does everything fall downward? It's as if there is a force pulling everything towards the centre of the Earth.'

And there is. That force is gravity. It pulls everything towards the centre of the Earth. Everything has a force of gravity. The bigger it is, the bigger the force. But the biggest, nearest thing to you is the Earth. Without gravity, nothing would stay on Earth that wasn't nailed down.

Fascinating facts

● A newton, the unit of force, is about the same as the weight of a medium-sized apple.

Living upside-down

Try this. Draw a circle on some paper. That's the Earth. Now draw some people standing on the Earth. A dozen people or more. Finished? Now read this.

What do your people look like?

Are they standing mostly on the top of the Earth?
It's hard to imagine that people live all over the Earth. It's much easier to think that they are living just on the top half – standing up.

Are the people all over the Earth, but those on the 'sides' and 'bottom' of the Earth lying down?
It's hard to imagine that people can actually stand up on the bottom or the sides of the Earth. Much easier to imagine that they lie down all the time.

Have you drawn people all over the Earth standing up, so they stick out like the prickles on a hedgehog?
That's right. It's hard to believe, but people live all over the Earth. If they didn't, we wouldn't be watching all those television soaps from Australia!

Now put a dot in the very middle of your circle. That's the centre of the Earth. Wherever you are on the Earth, down is towards this centre. Now you can draw people all over the Earth, sticking out in every direction.

That's why Newton's apple fell downwards. It was falling towards the middle of the Earth – the Earth's centre of gravity.

The Earth's gravity is pulling down on us all the time. We call that pull your weight. You have weight because the Earth's gravity is pulling down on your mass. The mass is the stuff you are made from. Your mass stays the same, wherever you are. But your weight can change.

If you went to another planet, the pull of gravity would change. If that planet were bigger than the Earth, the pull would be stronger. If it were smaller than the Earth, the pull would be weaker.

What's keeping you down?

Gravity is an invisible force that holds us on the Earth. We can't see it, but we can see its effects. Why don't we feel it? Usually, it is too weak to feel. But it gets stronger the more stuff there is in something.

So jumping off the Earth is like a reverse bungee jump! (Except that the force gets weaker the further you go.)

What's the biggest thing in your life? How close is it? You might think it's your life partner or your favourite team. But the biggest and nearest thing in your life is the Earth. The pull of the Earth is strong for two reasons. The Earth is very, very big – it weighs six billion trillion kilograms. And the Earth is very, very close to you – you're standing on it!

The nearer you are to the centre of the Earth, the more you weigh. That is because you are closer to the centre of gravity. At the bottom of a valley, you weigh a little more than you do at the top! The further you are from the centre of the Earth, the less you will weigh. You are further from the centre of gravity. Climb to the top of a mountain and you lose weight (but not mass). Sadly, you will still weigh the same on the bathroom scales when you come down…

Dealing with the force of gravity

Gravity shapes our bodies. We are the shape we are because of gravity. We need muscles and bones, shaped as they are, to keep our body shape against the pull of gravity. Sometimes we feel forces stronger than the force of gravity. When we are on a big dipper, or take a tight corner in a car, there are forces on our bodies several times the force of gravity.

Pilots and astronauts are trained to take strong gravity forces. They may ride on the end of a huge roundabout that spins them faster and faster. They feel a force several times the force of gravity.

Fascinating facts

- Your ear is the organ that senses the pull of gravity. It can be exciting to feel the movement on a big dipper. But when you are weightless, or when you feel very strong 'G' or gravity forces, you may feel sick.

Fascinating facts

- The twice-daily rise and fall of sea level is caused by the gravitational pull of the Moon, and also of the Sun.

- The heavier something is, the greater its force of gravity. The Earth weighs about six billion trillion tonnes. That's a lot of gravity!

Can heavy things fall slowly?

Everyone finds it very hard to believe that light and heavy things, dropped together, can hit the ground together. Even when you've seen it, you may not believe it! The Earth pulls harder on things of greater mass, and you might expect them to fall faster. But their greater mass means they're harder to get moving (just compare pushing a bicycle with bump starting a car) and these two just about cancel each other out. Whatever the mass, objects fall at the same speed.

The exception, of course, is where one object has a greater surface area than another, catching the wind. A sheet of paper will float to the ground more slowly than a screwed-up ball; a feather will fall much more slowly than a hammer. The Moon astronauts graphically demonstrated what happens without the slowing effects of the air. A feather on the airless Moon dropped at the same speed as a hammer.

You are heavy, but you can slow down your fall!

If you jumped from an aeroplane, you would make a very sticky mess when you hit the ground. Yet people jump from aeroplanes every day. They survive because they are wearing a parachute. The parachute slows them down and they land safely.

The parachute makes you much bigger. It doesn't weigh much, but it is big enough to fill with air and the air slows you down. The drag of the air holds you back.

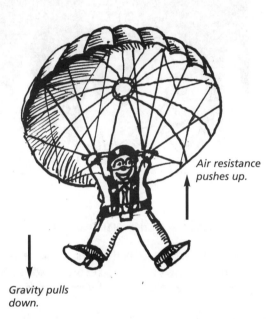

Air resistance pushes up.

Gravity pulls down.

Can you ever escape gravity?

Stand by for take-off. Stand by for the great tug-of-war. On the down team – gravity! On the up team, the lift from the aeroplane. But how will we give the aeroplane lift? Of course! Engines to full throttle. If enough air flows over the wings, fast enough, the aeroplane will go up.

We're rushing forward. Air is streaming over the wings. Because of their special shape, they're giving us lift. Gravity loses. The aeroplane is climbing.

Whoops! We're out of petrol. The aeroplane is slowing down. The air over the wings is slowing down, too. We haven't enough lift. Gravity is winning! Stand by for a crash landing!

Wherever we are in the vicinity of the Earth, gravity is pulling on us.

So although an aeroplane may seem to give us a few moments of freedom from gravity's pull, it can never free us from the inevitable return to Earth. Only a powerful space rocket can do that – and then only once we are so far from the Earth's pull that other heavenly bodies are pulling on us harder. Even space debris, apparently freed from the Earth's attractive forces, is in slow free fall towards us again. So mind your head!

Gravity pulls on the planets

The planets are moving around the Sun. Some of the planets have moons orbiting around them. Others have rings. All these are held in space by the force of gravity.

- Gravity keeps the planets in orbit round the Sun.
- Gravity keeps the Moon in orbit round the Earth.
- Gravity keeps the rings in place round Saturn, Neptune and Uranus.

The Moon orbits the Earth's centre of gravity. But Pluto has such a big moon, Charon, that Pluto and Charon both orbit a point in space between them, like a pair of dancers holding hands.

Centre of gravity

Isaac Newton first said that everything that had mass had gravity. So everything has a centre of gravity, too. The Earth's centre of gravity is at its very middle.

A tall object may have a high centre of gravity. This means it would be easy to push over. Tall vehicles such as double-decker buses have all their heavy bits – the engine and axles – as low as possible, so that the centre of gravity is really low. A double-decker bus will lean a long way before it falls over!

Your centre of gravity changes as you move. If you stand up, it is high up in your body. If you lie down, it is close to the ground. When a gymnast is on the bar, her centre of gravity is constantly changing.

Weightlessness

All this gravity stuff is great. But how would you get on without it? If you go far enough into space, you can be so far from any planets or stars that their gravity hardly pulls on you at all. You will be almost weightless. You will float around with no up or down.

Fascinating facts

- When two huge ocean liners are docked next to each other, they are pulled towards each other by their force of gravity.

- A black hole is caused by a very dense object that has a massive gravitational field. This acts like a space funnel. Anything pulled into the space funnel can never escape, including light itself.

- Candles don't burn in weightless conditions. The waste gases don't float away. They collect around the wick as a sphere and put the candle out!

- Everest is the Earth's biggest mountain. It is the biggest mountain the Earth will ever have. The Earth's gravity would pull a bigger mountain down to the size of Everest.

Fascinating facts

● There's a hole in every bell-shaped parachute. It's there to let the air out. Without the hole, the parachute would swing from side to side. This would upset the gravity detectors in your ears, and you'd be sick!

Weightlessness – plus points

- You can sleep standing up. If there's no gravity pulling on you, what's the point in lying down?

- You can break every Olympic high jump record. There's no gravity to pull you down again.

- You will be taller. On Earth, gravity squashes the soft discs between the bones in your back. In space, these discs aren't squashed and you (temporarily) grow 2cm.

Weightlessness – minus points

- You will get a fat head. Because your heart is used to pumping blood up to your head against the force of gravity, it will carry on doing it. More blood reaches your head, just as if you had hung upside-down on Earth for a long time. (After some time, your body will get used to the new conditions. Your heart will beat around 10 times a minute slower.)

- Your legs will go all weak. Your muscles and bones support you on Earth but in space they have little to do, and go flabby.

- When you get back to Earth, it will take you a while to get used to gravity again – to get back to your usual height, to strengthen your legs and to shrink your head!

Can you move things without touching them?

There are other invisible forces like gravity. Magnetism is an invisible force. Magnets can pull things and push things without touching them. Magnets pull things made from iron and steel and some other metals. Magnets can push on other magnets. Magnets can work through other materials. You can move paper-clips around with a magnet under the table. A strong magnet will even pull through your hand. And magnets will work through air and water (see Chapter 2).

Gravity is like magnetism. It works without touching. Even if you are flying in an aeroplane or swimming in the sea, the Earth's gravity is still pulling you down.

Comparing gravity and magnetism

	Gravity	Magnetism
Can it pull things together?	Yes	Yes
Can it push things apart?	No	Yes
Is it invisible?	Yes	Yes
Will it work with any two objects?	Yes	No

Fascinating facts

● Frogs can't jump in space. They somersault in the weightless conditions.

● Plants grow in a strange way in weightless conditions. The shoots grow towards the light, but the roots grow anywhere. Which way is down?

● Birds hatched in space wouldn't be able to fly properly. All they would be able to do is loop the loop.

Activities

Level One

Get the children to confirm that gravity acts on everything by simply letting them drop different objects and observe what happens to them. All fall towards the Earth, but some will bounce and some will not. Encourage the children to start to observe that similar objects fall in a similar time.

Level Two

Ask children to record the way different objects fall. Compare the fall of a sheet of scrap paper, the same sheet screwed up, a simple parachute and a parachute with additional weight attached. Start to agree and record general rules – for example, 'Big light things fall slowly'.

Level Three

Ask children to draw the Earth and the people living on it. Expect illustrations that do not represent the true picture – that the Earth's centre of gravity is in its very middle, and that for people all over the Earth the centre is 'down'. Discuss this, using a globe. Establish that gravity is a force that pulls you towards the centre of the Earth.

Level Four

Ask the children to compare the way that different objects of the same size but different weights, fall. For example, ask them to compare film canisters with differing amounts of modelling clay inside. They should find that generally the weight makes little difference, and the objects – since air resistance pulls on them all in the same way – hit the ground at the same moment.

This doesn't work perfectly because the air interferes. In a vacuum, or on the airless Moon, the canisters would fall at the same rate – as would a feather and a hammer. You could show the classic demonstration of this by Neil Armstrong on the surface of the Moon. (Show the programme 'Forces' in the TV series 'Making Sense of Science', from Channel 4 Learning.)

Level Five

Can a roller roll uphill? Ask children to follow these instructions.

Tape together two plastic funnels at their wide ends. Use two metre rules to make a track. Tape one end of the rules together so that the track becomes narrower towards the bottom. Hold the rules a little apart at the top end and roll the funnels on the track. Are they climbing up the track? Or going down it? The children will observe that the roller is actually going down, although the narrowing rules lift it as it progresses.

What slows you down?

Friction is a force that resists movement when one surface slides against another. Investigating friction in the classroom can throw up all kinds of anomalies. The results can be messy and confusing, and we may have difficulty explaining them to children.

Friction is a force that acts to slow down moving objects. When you rub your hands together, you can feel the action of friction. Friction slows the movement of your hands. Friction may produce heat. Friction may produce sound. In extreme conditions friction can produce light.

The important thing to remember is that **friction can act between any two surfaces, no matter how smooth they are.** Just think of bike brake blocks gripping a steel bike wheel. Both surfaces are fairly smooth, yet there is friction between them. This is partly because friction is a molecular effect – the grip between two surfaces that are microscopically rough. It is partly because two very similar surfaces often have high frictional grip on each other – think about the heat you generate by rubbing together your two (identical) hands!

So friction isn't a simple effect. To add to this, surfaces can behave differently when they are moving and when they are at rest. The same shoe that gives you a great jump-off in tennis may not behave so well when you skid to a halt.

Friction between surfaces

- You may get friction between two surfaces. They may not be rough surfaces. They may be smooth surfaces.

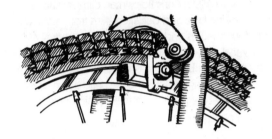

- You may get friction in air. Friction slows planes and parachutes. Smooth planes cut down the force of friction.

- You may get friction in water. Friction slows boats and fish. Smooth boats cut down the force of friction. Smooth fish cut down the force of friction.

What does this mean in practice?

In practice, this means that a shoe with a ridged and apparently grippy sole doesn't always grip as well as a shoe with a smooth sole – this will, after all, have more sole area in contact with the floor. It means that both soles will behave differently if you drag them over the carpet and put them on an angled board. The former is moving friction; the latter is stationary friction, or 'stiction'.

Just slow down a minute

There is friction between surfaces, but there is also friction between you and the air, or between you and water.

On 29 August 1996, Chris Boardman climbed aboard a strange looking bike and pedalled 4km from a standing start in four minutes and eleven seconds – nearly 60km an hour. Try that on your bike! You won't be able to get near it. Why not? Chris Boardman is extremely fit, of course, and has very strong legs. But he also had a very special bike made by Lotus, who also make racing cars and sports cars.

The big problem with going fast on a bike is not so much the speed at which you need to pedal as the way the air slows you down. You can feel air friction whenever you travel fast on a bike. It's the rubbing on your body as you pedal forward. It makes your clothes flap against your body. What Lotus did was cut that air friction down. They did it by looking at ways of streamlining Chris Boardman and his bike. To get it just right, they experimented in a wind tunnel.

The Lotus bike is made from carbon fibre – a strong, light, smooth material. The bike frame was made as simple as possible, and shaped so that the air just flowed over it. The back wheel was covered, so that the spokes didn't disturb the smooth flow of air over the bike.

Then they reshaped the rider. They made the handlebars low and narrow, so that Chris Boardman was crouched low, with his elbows close to his sides. He wore tight-fitting clothes, so that nothing flapped. His helmet ended in a long point, so that the air over his head swept on over his back.

From the front, Boardman and the bike were as small as they could be. Cutting air friction made a high speed possible.

Reducing friction

You can reduce friction. Water may make things move more easily because it is a lubricant. Sometimes, at low temperatures, water can act as a lubricant, reducing friction between surfaces. But water can make a car skid – as in this story:

Fighting friction

'I don't understand it,' said Dad. 'A policeman stopped me on my way to work today and told me my back tyres were bald. I've got to get them changed, or I shall be in trouble. But I watched the British Grand Prix on Saturday and all the tyres were bald.'

'There's a difference,' said Charley.

'What sort of difference?'

'Was it raining for the motor race?'

'No.'

'There you are, then,' said Charley. 'As long as it doesn't rain, bald tyres are fine. In fact, they're better than tyres with tread patterns on. All the tyre surface is touching the road. All the tyre grips the road. Great friction.'

'And if it rains?' said Dad.

'Then you are in trouble,' said Charley. 'The water gets between the tyre and the road and reduces the friction – the grip. You won't be able to go very well, to steer or to stop. You need slots in the tyre to pump out the water!'

'I suppose I'd better get some new tyres,' said Dad.

'Yes,' said Charley. 'Before it rains!'

Oil can make things move more easily as it also is a lubricant. Oil molecules are slippery. They enter the hollows on the surfaces, helping to smooth them out. These slippery molecules help to reduce friction.

What force is pulling your spinner down? This is gravity. What force is slowing it up? This is air friction, or air resistance. You can't change gravity, but how can you change the way air friction acts on your spinner?

Air friction

You can see the effects of air friction on an object using a paper spinner or a parachute. It's air friction that slows down parachutes. The air moves over the surface of the parachute – inside and out. This slows its fall.

Cartoons that show us falling parachutes can convince us that, as with Minnie Mouse's bloomers, it's the air inside the parachute that holds us back like a giant hand. But it's the air friction that counts, and we can see this if we drop a paper spinner, which has no bell to hold the air. The whirring wings of the spinner are slowing its fall by air friction.

So in principle, you could jump from an aeroplane hanging on to a giant spinner rather than a parachute; but the effects on you of high-speed rotation would be unpleasant to say the least. Try it with a model paper one instead – as in the activities for this chapter.

Fascinating facts

- The slots or sipes on car tyres squeeze out the water from under the tyre. They can spray gallons of water out every second, so that the part of the tyre in contact with the road, the footprint, is always dry.

- On ice, not even tyre patterns can get a good grip. There is almost no friction at all. In countries where cars travel a lot on ice, the tyres have studs that punch into the ice, giving them some grip.

- Car tyres wear out because they are always rubbing on the road. But roads wear out, too. The traffic is always rubbing away at the road surface.

- Some modern bikes are designed for the rider to be prone. The rider lies down and the pedals are in front of him. This makes the front of the bike smaller and reduces air friction.

Activities

Level One

Friction is not an easy or appropriate idea for very young children to tackle, but they can discuss ways in which they experience it themselves. For example, it may slow them if they try to come down the playground slide bare-legged. Their skin 'sticks' to the slide. There is a strong friction effect. They can reduce this effect by sliding down on a jumper or a mat.

Point out that they can push off the roundabout, or on a swing, because of the friction between their feet and the ground.

Level Two

Ask the children to compare the friction qualities of two different shoes. Find two different shoes, both about the same size. Choose one with a ridged sole, and one with a smooth one – for example, a trainer and a bedroom slipper. Put a few building bricks in the lighter shoe so they both weigh about the same – for fairness.

Now test the grip of the shoes in two ways. Try putting the shoes side by side on a plank, and lifting the end of the plank. Which slides first? Which has the better grip here?

Now test the grip of the shoes when you pull them along. Which is easier to pull? The slipper may not have the ridges of the trainer, but there is more of its sole in contact with the ground.

Level Three

Invite the children to investigate air friction by making a paper spinner and experimenting with it.

The children should cut out a spinner with two wings from a piece of paper. Tell them to bend down the wings slightly, but not very far. Invite the children to drop their spinners and watch what happens. If they have made them correctly, they will drop for a moment and then begin to spin to the ground. If they don't, the wings have probably been bent down too far. The spinner must be Y-shaped. Experiment with dropping the spinner. Try changing its weight, the shape of its wings, how it is folded and where it is dropped. Try making bigger and smaller spinners.

What force is pulling the spinner down? What force is slowing it up? Where is gravity in all this? Where is air friction? You can't change gravity, but can you change the way air friction acts on your spinner?

Level Four

Investigate friction in water. Ask the children to make small boats from sheets of plywood or balsawood, making the bows different shapes. They will find that streamlined shapes are easier to move. Let them explore this by seeing how much pull the different boats need or how much puff is needed to blow them along if they are fitted with a sail.

Level Five

Investigate ways of reducing friction. Tell the children to take a wooden brick and try dragging it across different surfaces. They should not necessarily expect the rougher surfaces to be most resistant – the brick may slide easily across the points of sand grains on sandpaper, for example.

Then ask the children to try dragging the brick across a waterproof surface. They should try the surface dry, with water on it and with a little oil (cooking oil). Ask the children to measure the pull needed with a newton meter, and to record their results.

Pushes, squeezes and springs

Balanced forces

Forces are around us all the time, even when things aren't moving. Two opposing sumo wrestlers aren't moving, but you can tell there are forces at work. They are sweating and straining. They are both putting the same amount of force into the fight. Neither is moving because both are pushing exactly the same amount. One is pushing with a force, and the other is pushing with the same force. The forces are in balance, and neither of them can move. Lots

of force – but no movement. But what's this? From somewhere, one of the wrestlers has summoned a little extra strength. Just a little, but it's enough. His opponent is moving backwards – the forces are not in balance any more. One last shove and yes! A champion is declared!

In the same way, two tug-of-war teams aren't moving. But there are forces at work. The forces are balanced. If a few more people joined the team on the left, the forces would be unbalanced. Which way would the flag on the rope be pulled?

You can't see the forces acting on a football. They're invisible. One is the force of gravity. Gravity is pulling the ball down towards the centre of the Earth. So why doesn't the ball go down? Something is stopping it. The ground is pushing back on the ball. Gravity and the push of the ground are in balance. The ball stays where it is!

When two forces are in balance, an object stays still. When you push against a wall, you may be quite still. You are pushing. The wall is pushing back. The forces are in balance. A space rocket on the launch pad has two forces acting on it – that of gravity pulling it down, and that of the launch pad pushing it up. These forces are in balance, and the rocket stays still. Until the engines start…

Floating and sinking

Some objects float in liquids. Some sink. Some objects can be made to float, or they can be made to sink.

Objects float when they are lighter than water. Even heavy objects can be made to float, as long as they are filled with air. The air makes them lighter than water. When things are lighter than water, the upthrust of the water holds them up. Gravity pulls down. The water pushes up. The two forces are in balance. The object stays still. It floats.

A floating object is in balance. The force of gravity is balanced by the upthrust of the water. As long as the object isn't too dense – when the force of gravity will exceed the upthrust of the water and the object will sink – the object will float, the forces on it nicely balanced.

Fascinating facts

- The longest tug-of-war in history lasted for two hours and fifty-one minutes. For all that time, the teams sweated and strained, but the forces were in balance, and neither team moved.

When are forces unbalanced?

When forces are unbalanced, things move. Take that space rocket. It is blasting off at John F Kennedy Space Centre. It is being held back by gravity, but gravity is a weak force compared with the tremendous thrust of the rocket engines. Because the forces are unbalanced, the rocket climbs into the sky.

When forces are unbalanced, things change shape. When you squeeze some modelling clay, the modelling clay pushes back. But if the modelling clay pushed back as hard as you squeezed, you could never change its shape.

Examining springs

Are you sitting comfortably? I mean REALLY comfortably? Are you sitting on a nice comfy sofa? Or are you slumped on a cosy bed? It's the coil springs in your chair or your bed that are making you comfortable.

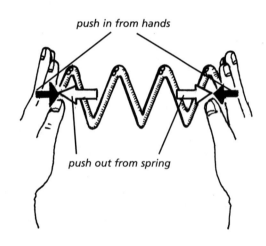

push in from hands

push out from spring

Stand up for a moment. Now sit down again slowly. Notice what happens. As you sit down the springs give and you squash them. The chair or the bed gets a dent in it the shape of your bottom. The forces are unbalanced. If the springs went on squashing, you would flatten the chair. But wait! Now the springs have stopped squashing. They won't squash any more. You are sitting on them, and the forces are balanced. The springs are pushing up just as hard as you are pushing down. You are sitting comfortably. But if you stand up again, the forces become unbalanced. The springs return to their original size.

Pogo sticks have springs that operate like this, too. The spring in the pogo stick is squashed by your weight. When it is released, it springs back, bouncing you into the air.

Springs and forces

Forces come in different sizes, and push and pull in different directions. Forces also make things change shape. Some things stay in their new shape, but others spring back to their previous shape. For example, if you push on a spring, it pushes back at you, and it quickly returns to its original shape.

When you have two forces, equal and opposite, acting on each other, the forces are balanced, and the object remains where it is. A ball on top of a spring has squashed the spring, but it isn't moving. The force that is pulling it down is the invisible force of gravity.

Are there springs around you now? There may be a spring that closes the door; there are bound to be springs in the lock. There are springs in the chair you are sitting on, and springs under the saddle of your bike. There may be springs holding your reading-lamp in place. There is even a spring on the shutter of a floppy disc!

Some springs are flat 'leaf' springs. Some are 'coil' springs. If you look at a stapler, you will see both. A flat leaf spring lifts the arm back after you have stapled something. A long coil spring pushes the next staple into place.

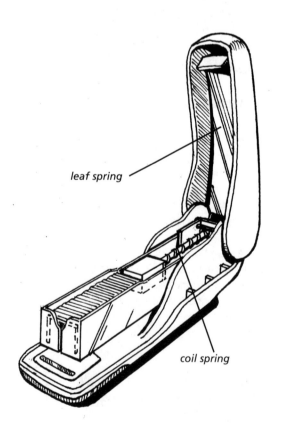

leaf spring

coil spring

Materials are springy because of the forces between their molecules. When you squeeze a spring, you push the molecules together. When you let the spring go, they jump apart again. When you stretch a spring, you drag the molecules apart. When you let it go, the molecules jump together.

At full stretch

A spring will not stretch forever. A spring finally reaches the point where it will no longer stretch. Scientists call this point the elastic limit. When a spring reaches its elastic limit, any more force will change it for good. It will not spring back to shape. If you go on stretching the spring beyond its natural limit, it snaps.

The same is true for stretchy or springy materials. Take a bar of modelling clay. It is stretchy stuff. Carefully bend the bar. Watch what happens. At first, the modelling clay bends. The modelling clay on the outside of the bar stretches, and the bar changes shape. Then the modelling clay reaches its elastic limit. It begins to break up. When modelling clay reaches its elastic limit, it will not go back to its original shape.

What happens to bubble gum and pizza cheese at their elastic limits?

Fascinating facts

- In 1676, the English physicist Robert Hooke discovered that things change shape the more they are pulled or pushed and that they get their shape back once the pull or push is removed. Unless, of course, they have been tested beyond their elastic limit.

- New plastic materials are being developed that behave as if they had a memory. You can squash them into a completely different shape, and they will return to their correct shape again.

The elastic limit

In 1940, the world's third longest suspension bridge was built across the Tacoma Narrows in Washington State, USA. It had been given the name 'Galloping Gertie' because in the four months after it was finished, winds caused its deck to bend and heave. Cars driving across it looked like ships at sea.

Then one morning, a wind (68km/hr) made the bridge bend and twist more than ever. The deck bent as far as it could, and then began to break up. Huge pieces fell into the river below. Fortunately, nobody was hurt, but a journalist who was crossing the bridge at the time had to get out of his car and crawl 150m to safety.

The bridge had resonated with the wind. It hummed with it until it broke.

Galloping Gertie had reached her elastic limit. She had bent and twisted as far as she could. When she was pushed even further, she broke up.

Pulling and stretching

A variety of other materials share the same properties as springs. Elastic, for example, has molecules that allow a stretch, and then recovery. This is how a bungee rope operates.

Stand here, please, on the edge of the bridge. You'll have to shuffle forward. You can't walk. The cords around your ankles stop that. You'll notice they are attached to the bungee rope behind you. It's very long and stretchy. We've measured it carefully. It's just long enough to give you a long fall, but not so long that you will end up in the river.

Don't look down! It's a long way down there. The best thing is just to look forward as you jump. What's going to happen? Well, you will free fall at first. Then the bungee rope will catch you and it will start to stretch. You will feel it pulling on you. Then, when the bungee rope is fully stretched, it will stop your fall, and you will bounce back up again – slowly at first, then in more and more bounces, smaller and smaller, until the forces on you are in balance. You will stop – you will just be hanging there.

Then we will lower you down slowly and they will pick you up in the boat. That's it – nothing to it. Oh, but you'd better put this helmet on in case of accidents. Not that it will be much use…

There are stretchy or springy materials all around you – for example, in a baby bouncer and the straps that hold things onto your bike. You'll also find them in gymnasium equipment, such as rowing machines. They are even in your clothes. Without the stretchy material in the waistband, your pants would fall down!

Your springy body

Your body has parts with a springy nature. If it didn't, you would have to move round like a robot. You wouldn't be able to jump, and you would not absorb the shock of landing.

When you run, your foot hits the ground with a force of two or three times your body weight. If you ran in a marathon, your foot would be hitting the ground like this 25,000 times. Without some sort of spring effect, your ankles and knees would be damaged by the forces.

There are bags of fluid in your joints which act like springs, absorbing some of this shock. But even they cannot stand endless pounding. This is why you should wear a cushioned springy shoe. Training shoes are designed to absorb the forces.

Springs for measuring

Every object has mass. The mass of an object is the amount of stuff in it. The Earth pulls on this mass with the force of gravity. We call this pull the object's weight. A spring balance measures the weight of an object. The object pulls the spring in the balance, moving the pointer. An object with a mass of 10g stretches the spring twice as much as an object with a mass of 5g.

We can also use a spring balance like this to measure force. Forces are measured in newtons, named after Sir Isaac Newton. When you pull an object along with a newton meter, you are measuring the force needed to move it in newtons. The symbol for the newton is N.

Fascinating facts

- Springy things bounce. Rubber is springy. So is steel and even glass. Glass marbles bounce because they change shape a tiny bit as they hit the floor.

- Cars have dampers, as well as springs. The dampers, or shock absorbers, slow down the movement of the springs. If they didn't, you would bounce over every bump. Without the dampers, the car would be comfortable, but very bouncy. You would feel as if you were in a small boat on a rough sea and you'd probably be sick.

- The world record bungee jump was from a helicopter. Gregory Riffi jumped above the Loire Valley in France in February 1992. The bungee rope stretched from 250m long to over 600m long.

- In parts of the world that suffer from earthquakes, tall buildings are built on springs. The springs absorb the force of the earthquake and prevent the building being knocked down.

Activities

Level One

Tell the children that they are going on a spring hunt! Ask them to look for springs around the classroom – but to mind their fingers! They may find them in a door-closer, the chair they sit in to read in the book corner, or the clamps in some kinds of files.

Some springs are flat 'leaf' springs. Some are 'coil' springs. Look at a stapler together so that the children can see both types. A flat leaf spring lifts the arm back after you have stapled something. A long coil spring pushes the next staple into place. Help the children identify each type of spring.

Level Two

Ask the children to compare the springiness of different elastic bands, both thick and thin. Which stretch the most – with care – and why? Then ask the children to hang elastic bands from the backs of chairs and test them with increasing weights – perhaps by putting wooden bricks in a carrier bag hung from the band. Warn the children that they must protect their eyes and keep their feet out of the way of falling bricks during this activity.

Level Three

Invite the children to explore springs that squash in bathroom scales and kitchen spring scales. Ask them to estimate and then measure the weight of 'mystery parcels' you have made by putting weights or wooden bricks inside a box.

Level Four

Encourage the children to explore and measure springs that stretch. They can use parcel scales of all sorts – and newton meters, which are adapted spring balances. How does the stretch vary with the weight? Encourage them to make estimates of weight. Ask them to think about how the thickness of the spring affects the way the scale can be used.

Level Five

Explore bounce. Bounce is a result of the springiness of materials – the speed with which they regain their shape. Even hard objects will be squashed by bouncing on the floor. Those that recover their shape fastest bounce highest. Ask the children to test and record the bounce of a range of school balls – from foam balls to cricket balls – dropped on the same surface from the same height.

Is a battery full of electricity?

Making a pile!

Alessandro Volta was a nobleman born in Como in northern Italy who was fascinated by electricity. He was curious about a discovery made by Luigi Galvani. Galvani had found that the legs of a frog would jerk when touched with two pieces of metal. Galvani thought that frogs, and other animals, made electricity of their own. This explained the way the legs jumped.

But Volta disagreed. Why should animals make electricity? Maybe the metals were making the electricity? He tried out his idea. If he put two different metals to his tongue, he felt a slight tingling. Was this electricity?

Then he read about an animal that could make its own electricity – the torpedo fish. This fish made a powerful electric shock that stunned smaller fish and made them easy to catch. The electricity came from discs of different materials inside the fish.

This gave Volta the idea of making a pile of copper and zinc discs which touched each other and a piece of wet leather. This first battery gave him a powerful electric shock, and it could do so over and over again. Napoleon was so impressed with Volta's electric pile that he made him a count and presented him with a medal. The Italian 10,000 lire bank note still has a picture of Volta on it.

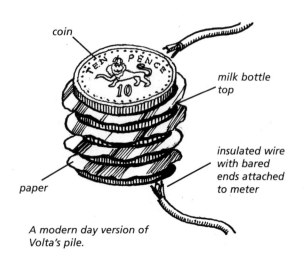

A modern day version of Volta's pile.

Humphry Davy used a pile made by dipping plates of copper and zinc into wooden boxes of salty water. By linking these together, they could produce a powerful electric current.

How does the battery work?

It's a common misconception that batteries are somehow full of electricity. Some children think that connecting them up in a circuit uses all this electricity up, and then the battery is empty (or 'flat'). But that's not how it is.

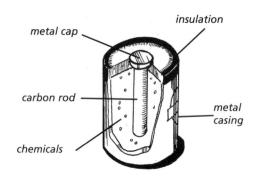

Electricity is a flow of minute particles called electrons, passed hand to hand like 'pass the parcel'. These electrons are in the materials that make up the circuit, but the battery provides the 'push' that makes the electrons flow.

The energy for the push of a battery comes from chemical reactions in the battery. It's when these chemicals have all changed and there is no longer the material for the chemical reaction that we say the battery is flat.

You might doubt that. You might think that in those neat little tubes there is electricity just waiting to pop out. But that's not what those first scientists found. They made an electric current with salt water and some bits of metal. And you can make one with a lemon!

Fruit and potato power

Think about this. Would you expect to find electricity stored in a lemon? It's unlikely. But a lemon contains the chemicals that – with the right combination of metals – will make the 'push' that will allow an electric current to flow – enough to make your tongue tingle or to power a digital watch. Don't doubt it – try it!

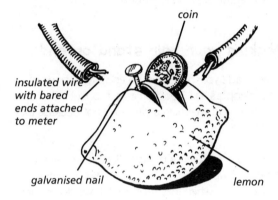

coin

insulated wire with bared ends attached to meter

galvanised nail

lemon

Cut two small slits in a lemon. The slits should be about 2cm long and 1cm apart. Shine a copper coin and a galvanised (zinc-covered) nail with sandpaper. Push one into each slit. Put a crocodile clip on each, with the wires loose. Carefully touch your tongue with the free ends of the wires. You should feel a tiny tingle. The lemon battery is producing current electricity (not to be confused with static electricity). You can connect an old digital watch to it and watch the time pass – lemon-powered.

Fascinating facts

- Because there was no way of measuring electricity three hundred years ago, scientists used their bodies as a test machine. They observed how far electricity went up their arm, or how far it went along a row of people holding hands.

Understanding the flow of electricity

The mistaken idea that electricity rushes out of the battery or the mains, dashes to the radio, does its job and goes home exhausted is not helped by the fact that a single cable operates most electrical appliances. Electricity apparently flows into the device, to be 'used up'. You might show the children a piece of unconnected two-strand wire to show that electricity flows to a device and back again. There are two wires inside the cable.

The way electricity flows is affected by the components in the circuit. The electric current in a circuit is exactly the same, wherever you decide to measure it. If there was electricity staggering back to the battery, you might expect there to be weak or strong points. But electricity flows a bit like water from a pump. The battery is the pump, pushing the electricity round.

Current electricity

So the electricity flows round the circuit. Electricity that flows is called 'current electricity'. Some of it comes from batteries – chemical pumps – that push the electricity around. But a much bigger and more powerful push comes from mains electricity; electricity that is generated by spinning turbines.

Some devices can use both mains and battery electricity. Transformers change high voltage mains electricity to low voltage electricity to operate many devices, including keyboards, computer accessories and many telephones. But the devices in the kitchen (such as the washing machine and the cooker) – and in other rooms around the house – are mains powered, and this electricity has the potential to kill.

It is essential to explain the safe use of mains electricity devices early. Many children will have routine home experience of their use. Do not encourage exploration or investigation of mains electricity. Explain that mains electricity is dangerous and can be lethal.

You are a conductor

Mains electricity can be dangerous, but it is even more dangerous if we are wet. Both our bodies and water are usually poor conductors of electricity. But a combination of high voltage and wet bodies can be lethal. The water increases your conductive qualities. There are special switches (cord pulls) in the bathroom – for the light, for example. They keep your wet hands away from the devices that switch current electricity on and off.

But don't give children the idea that all electricity is dangerous. They have to grow up in the real world, but they should be aware of basic safety rules.

Electricity safety

- Electrical devices for use in school have been tested beyond domestic standards. For example, the testers will have pushed metal objects inside the devices to see if it is possible to touch any 'live' bits. Do not use ordinary home devices in place of those sold by school suppliers in school.

- Annual safety checks are essential. Your local education authority or governors should arrange these.

- Remind children that it is never safe to touch live wires from the mains – even if they are planning to 'repair' them.

- You can get table-top transformers called low-voltage power supplies – children should be shown how to use them safely.

- Ordinary batteries should never be recharged. Never cut batteries open – they are full of chemicals, some of which are corrosive and could be harmful.

- Rechargeable batteries can be used again and again. However, they may give out a strong current if allowed to discharge quickly – through a short circuit, for example. Thin wires may get very hot. Don't mix different types of battery.

- Advise children against squeezing bulbs hard or screwing them too tightly into bulb holders. They are strong, but they do occasionally break. Some children may decide to use crocodile clips as earrings. However, they will only do this once as the springs in them are very strong!

Be Safe! is the ideal safety guide (ISBN 0 86357 081 X). A new edition was published in 2001 priced £5.50 (£5 to members). It is available from ASE, College Lane, Hatfield, Herts, AL10 9AA.

A fascinating sideline – static electricity

Static electricity – as opposed to current electricity – is not usually a curriculum topic. But it is fascinating and exciting – and it is a super subject if you are teaching about how our understanding of science has grown and developed. Static electricity has a long history and teaching about it can embrace ancient civilisations, historical scientists and thunderstorms.

Making your hair stand on end

Which film made your hair stand on end? Thousands of years ago, people's hair stood on end, too. But not because they were watching a film. And not because they met a dinosaur!

Ancient people treasured a pretty yellow stone called amber. When it was polished, it glowed. But something strange happened when they rubbed it. It would lift their hair. It attracted tiny scraps of dust. It was a magical stone.

Going nowhere

Amber is a fossil. It is from the trees that lived in the time of the dinosaurs. Its smooth yellow chunks are pieces of tree resin that has fossilised. Some of these chunks contain tiny animals and plants. Amber has a magical quality. When you rub it, it makes electricity.

This electricity isn't going anywhere. It's not like the electricity from a battery or the mains. It's static – staying still. It attracts things like dust, scraps and your hair. But a big charge of static electricity can jump and kill. The reason amber attracts like this is because rubbing knocks bits called electrons off it. That makes the amber a tiny bit electrically charged. And that attracts the dust.

Make your own static

There is static electricity all around you. On damp days it quickly goes to Earth, but on dry, frosty days you can rub a balloon on your jumper and stick it on the wall, or lift your hair in the air with it.

Tie a thread to two round balloons. Hang one under the table and give it twenty rubs with a woollen jumper. Now rub another balloon, hold it by the thread and bring it close to the first balloon. The static charges on the two balloons are both negative, and as the balloons get closer, they repel each other! Comb your hair, or rub your comb hard with a cloth. Run a tap so that you get a thin stream of water. Bring the comb close to the stream and watch it bend. Static electricity has attracted it!

Don't try this at home!

People used to believe that storms were sent by the gods. Vikings thought that the god Thor made storms by hurling his hammer from his chariot. The Romans buried unlucky people killed by lightning on the spot where the gods had killed them. But an American called Benjamin Franklin thought differently. He thought lightning was some kind of electricity and he risked his life to prove it.

Come back 250 years and meet him. He is standing inside a wooden shed, staying dry in a thunderstorm. In his hand he has a kite string. The kite is high in the sky, where its point will attract lightning. Its wet string will become a conductor of electricity, so Franklin is holding a handle made of dry silk, to insulate himself.

The lightning cracks and Franklin notices that strands from the string spring out. He reaches his hand out towards a door key hanging from the string. Crack! Sparks shoot to his hand. The kite and the thunderclouds are charged with electricity!

Fascinating facts

- You can be struck by lightning and live. Roy Sullivan, a park ranger from Virginia, USA, was struck by lightning seven times in his life, and survived! The lightning takes the shortest path through your body to the Earth. As long as the lightning path doesn't pass through your heart, you should survive.

- Electricity is dangerous. Even static electricity can kill if the charge is great enough. In 1753, George Wilhelm Richmann attempted to copy Benjamin Franklin's experiment with lightning. It killed him.

Lightning strikes!

Why is there static electricity in storm clouds? Perhaps a water droplet could explain.

 'Hi! I'm Wilma the water droplet. I've had a tough time the last few days, down here on Earth. It's been so hot, I've been totally vaporised! Of course, I can't stick around in that condition. Any passing breeze can pick me up. In a moment, I'm up on cloud nine.

It's chilly up there. I might condense – joining up with my neighbours to form drops. Or I can even freeze!

It's crowded up there in the thundercloud. We're jostling for space. I get rubbed up against other ice crystals and water droplets. We get a real charge out of this. In no time the whole cloud is humming with static electricity. All we need now is some point to life.

And there's one, down there! A pointed copper strip on top of a tower. There's a crack, a flash, and all that charge has leapt to Earth. That's lightning!'

Shocking experiments

'Welcome, ladies and gentlemen, to entertainment in the eighteenth century. We don't have television, so we have to make our own fun!

I need a row of volunteers. Step forward, please! Thank you. Now, all hold hands. The first person in the row, please put your hand to this device. It is called a Leyden jar. Inside it I have stored the electricity from rubbing together glass and leather many hundreds of times. Touch the jar, please. Bang!

Thank you. As you will observe, they've all fallen over. Notice how their hair is standing on end. Isn't that funny!

What's that? The gentleman at the far end appears to be dead? Ah well, you can't please everybody.'

Leyden jars (named after the university in Holland where they were invented) store up static electricity, releasing it all at once. Inside a Leyden jar is an electrode in contact with water or mercury. The outside electrode is in contact with water or mercury. One of the inventors felt the shock of that charge. 'In a word, I thought it was all up with me,' he said later.

Great stuff, this elektron

The Greek word for amber is elektron and so when an English scientist investigated amber 400 years ago, he called the stuff he investigated 'electricity'. But remember that static and current electricity are very different.

Fascinating facts

- In 1778, an umbrella was invented to protect you from lightning. A lightning conductor on the top, and a chain hanging down, conducted the lightning to Earth!

- If you are caught out in the open during a thunderstorm, curl up and try not to leave any pointy bits sticking out. Static electricity loves to jump to long points. That's why golfers can get struck – on the golf club.

Activities

Level One

It's important to begin a study of electricity with safety information. Teach children about the differences between safe battery electricity and dangerous mains electricity. Ask them to name examples of electrical devices around them – in the garage, kitchen and living room – and to try to imagine the world without electricity.

Ask the children to record the electrical devices you have in the classroom – and how you make them safe.

Level Two

Introduce the full circuit – battery to bulb and back to battery again. Show how breaking the circuit at any point extinguishes the bulb.

Ask the children to remove the bulb – making what is called an 'open' circuit – and to put different objects in the gap to see which are conductors and which are insulators.

Ask the children to record the different groups in two columns. Point out that other things – including your body and water – can conduct electricity – especially big currents. This is why touching a switch with wet hands is dangerous.

Level Three

Ask the children to make a full circuit. They can use a battery to light a bulb, to spin a motor, and to make a buzzer buzz. Ask what happens when you change the direction of the current. Try reversing the wires on the battery. Does the bulb still light? What happens to the motor? Does the buzzer work one way round only?

Use the circuit in a model lighthouse, model doorbell or electric fan.

Level Four

Ask the children to make up a circuit that lights one bulb. Then ask them to use another bulb and holder, and another wire, and light that too. What do they notice? Can they add another bulb and wire? What happens?

Do lights in a house work like this? No – because turning one light off leaves the rest on! For lights like these, you need to make a parallel circuit. Each bulb has a circuit of its own. If you take one bulb out, the rest will stay on.

Ask the children to record their circuits using the recognised symbols.

Level Five

Give the children a tiny motor, two thin wires and a bulb. Ask them to join them up in a circuit, so that the motor is taking the place of the battery. Then ask them to take a thin, strong thread (button thread is ideal) and wind it once round the pulley on the motor. They should hold the motor firmly, and pull the short end of the thread sharply to spin the motor. Direct them to watch the bulb.

The children are moving the magnets in the motor to generate their own electricity. Ask them to find out more about how electricity is generated – and the role of coal, oil and renewables in its production.

What makes bulbs brighter?

Complete circuits

A circuit must be complete for the electricity to flow. All the components, linked in a complete circuit, are needed for a bulb in the circuit to light. Look closely at a torch light bulb (when the torch is off!). The wire filament inside is part of the circuit. The electricity flows right through the bulb.

Electric current has a direction – from the negative to the positive terminal of the battery. When it was first investigated it was thought that it flowed from positive to negative. However, this has now been shown not to be the case. And it certainly doesn't flow in both directions at once (the idea of 'clashing currents' that children sometimes hold) despite the battery having two terminals.

Measuring electricity

The push of electricity is measured in volts – named after Alessandro Volta. Small batteries like those in a torch or a personal stereo are 1.5 volts. This is so small that (like Volta) you would have to put wires from the battery to your tongue to feel the electricity. But a 12 volt car battery will give you a shock that will jolt you. And mains electricity at 240 volts will throw you across the room and possibly kill you.

An analogy of an electrical circuit

You may need to use an analogy to explain the flow of electricity in a circuit to children. There is evidence that analogies help children to understand the invisible flow of electricity, but no analogy is perfect.

Use a loop of rope to represent the circuit. A child pushing the rope round in a circle represents the battery. If another child in the ring holds the rope more tightly, they create a resistance. They are behaving like a light bulb. An analogy of a switch would be a very tight grip on the rope – a resistance that no amount of pushing will overcome.

There are other models you could use – for example, soldiers marching round and round, getting their orders

and directions in a castle (battery) on the way, or lorries racing round a circular track with loads. The water flow analogy commonly compares the battery with a boiler, the bulb with a radiator and the wires with pipes. The analogy is imperfect. The battery is rather more like a water pump, and cutting the circuit, by breaking the pipe, will not stop the water flow!

Bulbs

On its way round a circuit, the electricity does some work. It may be squeezed through a thin wire inside a glass bulb. This makes it get hot and glow. The bulb lights

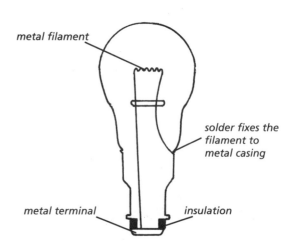

metal filament

solder fixes the filament to metal casing

metal terminal   insulation

up. The bulb lights because the moving electrons collide with the fixed atoms in the thin filament wire (the filament wire resists the flow of the electrons). The moving electrons transfer energy from the battery to the bulb. The bulb glows – because it is in a glass globe that contains no oxygen, it can't burn away.

The wiring inside the bulb completes a full circuit. The more electricity flowing through the bulb, the brighter the bulb is. Children may think that a large battery will make a bulb brighter. Higher voltage batteries do tend to be larger, but size alone is not an indicator of voltage – for example, 1.5V batteries exist in several different sizes.

You can put more than one bulb in a circuit. If one bulb follows another, we call it a series circuit.

More than one bulb

Putting more than one bulb in a circuit leads to challenges for children. Which bulbs will light? How brightly will they light?

Two bulbs in series double the resistance in the circuit. Both bulbs are dimmed compared with a single bulb. Provided both bulbs are the same, they will both glow equally. Many children believe that electricity will flow round the circuit as far as the first bulb, light that, and then 'stop'. They may believe that the first bulb in the circuit will 'use up' the electricity before it reaches the second, so that one bulb is brighter than the other.

In fact, both bulbs will shine equally brightly, but less brightly than a single bulb. The resistance of the two bulbs in this series circuit is greater than one bulb, and the current in the circuit is less. But this reduction is the same in every part of the circuit. So there is the same current in each bulb.

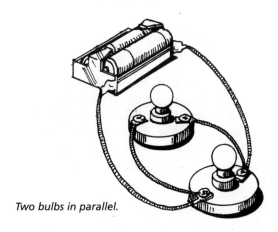

Two bulbs in parallel.

There are several ways of making a circuit so that both bulbs shine equally brightly, but you have to give each bulb a different circuit. When two bulbs are connected in parallel, the current divides equally between them. The 'push' to each bulb is equal. They shine equally brightly. They will shine as brightly as a single bulb because the current is now twice as large. One bulb will shine without the other because it is still in a complete circuit.

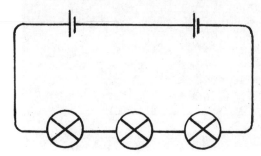

Three bulbs (and two cells) in series.

Switches

Circuits usually contain switches. You can make or break a circuit with a switch, and control the flow of electricity. Switches need to be made from a conducting material, and may need to be boxed in an insulating material.

Many children cannot explain how a switch works. Those who attempt to explain it may think that the electricity 'runs up' the wire when the switch is on, and 'runs back' when the switch is off.

Using symbols for circuits

The symbols we use for drawing circuits are those that are used by electrical engineers. They were not made for educational purposes, and their use raises some problems. This is because the symbols were designed to show circuit construction; they were not designed to illustrate differences between 'live' circuits, with electricity flowing through them, and 'dead' ones. The symbols represent, but do not illustrate, the circuits children plan and make. So all wires are represented by straight lines. Even a tangle of wiring will be shown as neat lines. Circuit diagrams are rather like the London Underground map – they do not show twists and turns.

Bulbs are represented as a cross in a circle – on or off. This is a 'lamp' in electrical terms. You may come across other ways of illustrating a bulb – for example, when one is used as a tracer, showing that something has been left on, rather than as a source of light. Teach children to use the cross symbol.

Cells are represented by a long and a short bar. The long bar represents the longer line of the + (plus) side of the cell; the short bar the line of the shorter – (minus) side. Two or more pairs form a battery. The gap between the bars represents the chemical reaction that takes place to produce the energy that pushes the electricity round the circuit. You can represent a battery with two or more sets of cells.

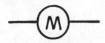

A motor is represented by an 'M' in a circle.

A buzzer is represented by a semicircle with two wires emerging from the curved side.

It is the representation of a switch that causes the biggest headaches. Since a switch is simply a break in a wire, it is represented open as an open door or gate. Closed, it should be represented just as a wire. (Remember that it is of no consequence to electrical engineers whether the circuit is live or not.) As a result, the switch disappears when it is closed. You may find it best to represent a switch with 'blobs'. This both emphasises it when open and shows where it is when closed. This is not strictly accurate to the symbol code, but follows the convention that shows a three-way junction 'blobbed'. Children would not be penalised for representing a switch with blobs in statutory examinations.

Troubleshooting

Follow these basic rules to ensure a circuit works.

- Make sure that the batteries you use are not flat.
- Match the battery to the component. A 1.5V bulb will be blown by a 4.5V battery, for example.
- Some motors may not spin without a higher voltage than 1.5V. The voltage is marked on each component in minute letters. (It can help to mark components with the working voltage, using nail varnish. A blob of pink on a bulb tells you that it is a 3V bulb, for example.)

If the circuit does not work, check on the connections.

- Are the bulbs screwed fully into the holders?
- Are bared wires tightly screwed to bulb holders or crocodile clips?
- Is the battery flat?
- Do the components match?

Don't panic. Always expect a simple solution.

Changing circuits

Changing the components in a circuit can change the flow of electricity and the way the circuit behaves. Lights may shine more brightly or dimly. Adding more bulbs will dim all of them. The buzzer will work, but only if it is put in the circuit one way round. The motor may turn while the bulb doesn't light up – small motors need less electricity than a bulb.

Fascinating facts

- Michael Faraday believed that children should share in the wonders of science. In 1825 he started the Christmas Lectures for Children at the Royal Institution, and they are still popular today. Every Christmas they are broadcast on television, something that would have been impossible without his invention of electricity generation.

- You will find Michael Faraday on old £20 bank notes. He is shown lecturing at the Royal Institution. The machine in front of him is an electricity generator. If you look carefully, you will see magnets and magnetic field patterns all over the note!

- Electric power stations produce electricity at 25,000 volts. This is actually increased to transmit it with minimal waste, to 400,000 volts. It is only reduced to mains level when it reaches a substation. Electricity of this strength can jump gaps. This is why it is so dangerous for children to play near power lines.

Electricity and magnetism

The relationship between electricity and magnetism is very close. An electric current in a wire has a magnetic effect, deflecting a magnetic compass, or producing patterns in iron filings. Michael Faraday recognised that moving a magnet might produce an electric current in a wire and this is the basis of generators and dynamos. Reversing a tiny electric motor turns it into a generator; it produces a small but measurable current. But electric turbines are huge and the electricity they produce is immensely powerful. It has to be 'transformed' to a voltage to use in your house. Even then, it can be lethal.

Mains electricity

Your television, computer, washing machine and cooker use electricity that comes to your house through cables. At the other end of those cables is a power station and it generates electricity for you to use. The power station uses the invention of Michael Faraday, the Father of Electricity.

Before Faraday, people knew that bringing an electric wire close to a compass made the magnetic needle move. But it was Faraday who first discovered how this might help generate electricity, over 150 years ago. He thought 'If electricity plus magnetism produces movement perhaps movement plus magnetism will produce electricity.' He tried moving a magnet near a wire. Sure enough, it generated a current.

As long as you can make the magnets move – using a steam turbine, moving water or the power of the wind – you can generate electricity. Electricity provides convenient energy and that's why it is so useful. Imagine that your television could be steam-powered, or your hair dryer was operated from a gas pipe. You could expect a few practical problems! But using coal or gas to generate electricity brings the energy to you through a handy, bendy wire; it goes where you want it, doesn't create smoke, and can be turned on and off at will.

So electricity is a kind of 'secondary' energy. It needs another source – whether a fossil fuel, falling water, turning windmill blades or nuclear power – to generate it. But get a turbine spinning – by anything from a hydro-electric dam to your bicycle wheel – and you will generate electricity.

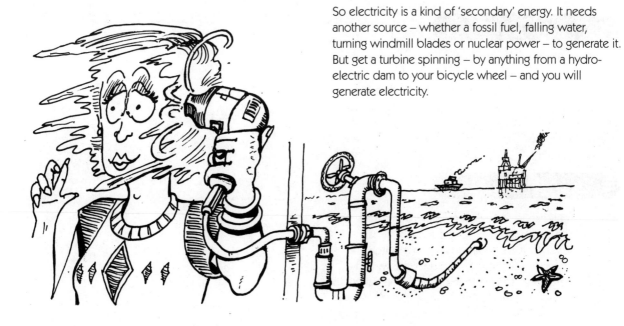

Activities

Level One

Encourage the children to observe how different combinations of bulbs and batteries give different levels of brightness and to suggest possible reasons for this.

Level Two

Get the children to add more bulbs to a circuit. Encourage them to notice the way the brightness changes as they add more bulbs.

Ask the children to make circuits that will light a bulb, run a motor, and buzz a buzzer. Ask for circuits where it is possible to switch a bulb on and off, to light a bulb and run a motor, with two or more bulbs in it. Ask whether the bulb will be bright or dim.

NOTE: The order of the components does not matter. A circuit containing a cell, a bulb and a switch will work the same, no matter where you put each component or how close together or far apart they may be. Emphasise this to the children. Remember that you can have more than one switch in a circuit, but they all have to be closed for the current to flow. However, for a buzzer to work the circuit must be the right way round.

Level Three

Challenge the children to find other ways of varying the current in a circuit. They could try combinations of a bulb and a buzzer, or a bulb and a motor. They may find that one works while the other doesn't. This can be due to one of the components – usually the bulb – not having enough current to light up and so behaving like a wire.

Level Four

Invite the children to make their own electromagnets. They should wind a thin insulated wire round a large nail, making the winding even – like thread on a cotton reel. Then they need to touch the two ends of the wire to a battery. They should NOT hold the wires to the battery for too long. They are making a 'short circuit' and the battery will run down very quickly. The wires might get hot, too!

Ask the children to use the electromagnet to pick up pins and paper-clips. Ask them what happens when you take the wires away from the battery.

Level Five

Ask the children to explore ways of making the bulbs shine brighter. You can get them to add more batteries, or to explore parallel circuits where each bulb has its own circuit.

First, ask the children to make a single circuit with a bulb in it. They should then attach a wire to each side of the bulb holder and extend the wires out to another one, so that this bulb has its own circuit, independent of the first one. Then tell them to add another ring beyond this one – and another, if you like. With bulbs in parallel the resistance reduces each time you add a circuit and each bulb will draw the same current, so stay as bright as before. If they formed a 'daisy chain' with the bulbs, the resistance would increase and the bulbs would dim. The children can try removing bulbs from the circuit or making breaks in different places to see what the effect is.

Our place in space

For many reasons, teaching about the Earth in space is not easy. Children come to school with their own ideas about space, and some of those ideas are very difficult to dislodge.

They may believe, for example, that the Sun moves and the Earth stands still. Given that the Sun apparently moves across the sky, this is understandable. Although the idea was questioned by Copernicus and later disproved by Galileo, the movement of the Sun was accepted science until the fifteenth century. This reflects our own observation, of course. Other commonly-held incorrect ideas include the theory that the Moon covers the Sun at night; that the shadow of the Earth is what causes the apparent change in the shape of the Moon; and that the Sun is slightly further away from the Earth in the winter (when in fact the opposite is true during the UK winter).

Where the Earth, Sun and Moon are concerned, there are three important concepts to tackle. With these understood, the relationship of Earth, Sun and Moon becomes clear.

Three important concepts

1 Size

The Earth, Sun and Moon are all spherical, of course – a function of the force of gravity which pulls all matter towards the centre of an object. Since the heavenly bodies are subject to their own force of gravity, they are all pulled towards their middles, and so tend to be ball-shaped. Very small objects in space don't have this big gravity force and so are irregular in shape. Furthermore, the heavenly bodies are subject to other gravity forces. The Sun's gravity makes the Earth and all the other planets keep orbit. Earth's gravity makes the Moon keep orbit, and so on.

Because books need to fit all three into a small picture, we have little idea of their relative sizes. You could fit a million Earths into the Sun. The differences are, literally, astronomical.

	Circumference	**Diameter**
Sun	4,370,880km	1,392,000km
Earth	40,076km	12,756km
Moon	10,915km	3,476km

2 Distance

If you model the Sun with a beach ball, the Earth is about the size of a pea and the Moon, the size of a peppercorn. Then the Earth and Sun are 40m apart. In reality, the Earth is about 152 million km from the Sun.

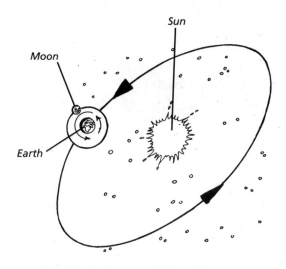

3 Movement

The Sun is actually moving, together with the whole solar system and the galaxy – and spinning, too. But for the sake of simplicity, let's imagine it is still. The Earth orbits it and, as it does so, the Earth is spinning. Both orbit and spin are counter-clockwise viewed from above. The orbit gives us our year; the spin gives us day and night.

The Moon is orbiting us. Since it always has its face turned towards us, the back of the Moon (incorrectly called the 'dark' side) is constantly away from us. For this to happen, the Moon has to spin as well as orbit. Rotation and orbit are synchronised. The Moon's orbit is not in the plane of the other planets. Since it bobs up and down, it can appear in many places in the sky (and during both day and night, though it is blotted out by the Sun's brightness as often as not). The Moon is not a light source. It reflects the Sun's light and, because of its orbit, it sometimes appears as a full Moon and sometimes as a new Moon, with all the phases in between.

It's a round world

It's 2,200 years ago. You are standing in the Egyptian city of Syene, close to a deep well. Next to you is an Egyptian scientist. His name is Eratosthenes, and he is waiting for midday.

'Look!' he says, and together you peer down the well. The light is shining to the very bottom. 'See that! Now, if the Earth is flat, the Sun should be shining to the bottom of every well in the world at this moment!'

'And is it?'

'Certainly not. In Alexandria, to the north, the Sun isn't lighting up the wells at all. I've been in Alexandria at midday and I know. In fact, the Sun is casting shadows there right now, because it isn't overhead.'

'Why is that?' you ask.

'It's obvious!' says Eratosthenes. 'It's because the world is round!'

Eratosthenes was right!

There are other ways of showing that the Earth is round:

- You can travel round the world.
- When ships appear over the horizon, they come over a curve. You see their masts first, then their funnels, and the hull last of all.
- When there is an eclipse of the Moon, the curved shadow of the Earth is cast on the Moon's face.
- The Earth is a planet. We can see that other planets in space are not flat.
- Pictures from artificial satellites show that the Earth is a sphere – the shape of a ball. We have only had pictures like these for the last 40 years.

The Earth

We think of the Earth as a solid rock, but it is more like a soft boiled egg. The hard shell is the crust – a thin, rocky layer that is four-fifths covered in water. Beneath that is the white of the egg – the mantle of mostly solid rock. In the centre of the Earth is the hot iron and nickel core, like the yolk of the egg.

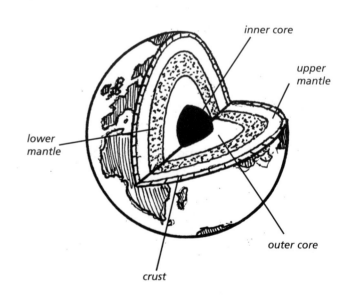

inner core

upper mantle

lower mantle

outer core

crust

Day and night

The Earth spins on its axis. Every 24 hours, it makes one complete rotation. It rotates anticlockwise, seen from above. We call this complete turn a day. Part of the Earth is always facing the Sun. This part is in daylight. But part will be facing away from the Sun. For this part of the Earth, it is night-time. As the Earth spins, each part of the Earth moves from light to dark and back to light again – from day to night, and back to day. From the Earth, it looks as though the Sun is moving across the sky. But it is the Earth that is turning, while the Sun stands still.

Copernicus and Galileo

In 1633, Galileo, the great astronomer, was forced to sign a declaration. 'I, Galileo Galilei, altogether abandon my false opinion that the Sun is the centre of the world and immovable and that the Earth is not the centre of the world and moves…' Exactly 360 years later, the Pope admitted that Galileo had been right. The Earth did, indeed, circle the Sun. Why did he do that? Because Galileo had proven it conclusively. But it doesn't look like that.

Have you ever taught in a sunny classroom? It can be hard to work and you may feel sleepy. Which is the sunniest classroom in your school? You could find out in different ways. If you know your school well you may remember one room or area which gets very sunny on hot days.

From the evidence of your eyes, which of these is true?

- The Sun moves across the sky, making different classrooms sunny in the morning and in the afternoon.
- The Earth turns so that the Sun appears to move across the sky, making different classrooms sunny in the morning and in the afternoon.

Both could be true. There are different ways of interpreting the same evidence, and it was these different interpretations that put Galileo in court.

What really happens?

Galileo got into trouble because people didn't believe him. They believed the evidence of their own eyes. They saw the Sun rise, climb into the sky, sink, set, dip below the horizon. They believed they saw a moving Sun.

But the Sun doesn't move. The Sun stays still, and the Earth moves. To us on the moving Earth, this looks exactly the same as a moving Sun. No wonder people were confused!

Hazel on the train

Hazel was sitting in a train with her mum. She looked out of the window on her left. She could see into another train. She looked out of the window on her right. She could see the station. There were people standing on the platform. She looked back to her left. The windows of the train next to her were moving slowly past her window.

'That train is leaving the station!' she said to her mum.

'No, dear,' said her mum. 'That train is standing still. WE are leaving the station!'

Hazel looked to her right. Sure enough, they were passing the people on the platform. Her train was moving.

Hazel's train is like the Earth, and the other train is like the Sun. Hazel's train is moving, and the other train is standing still.

Fascinating facts

- The Earth is both spinning and moving around the Sun. It spins at more than 1,600km an hour. It also travels round the Sun at over 100,000km an hour. We don't sense this movement. For us, the Earth feels as though it is standing still.

- Our Sun is a star. There are as many stars in our galaxy as there are people on Earth; and there are as many galaxies in the Universe as people on Earth, too. And our Sun is a very insignificant star, in a very small galaxy.

- The Sun is a gigantic light source. Its surface is at a temperature of over 5,000°C. In the centre, where nuclear reactions are turning hydrogen to helium, the temperature is 15 million degrees Celsius. Although the Sun is around 150 million kilometres from us, its light can still harm your eyes if you look straight at it. Light from the Sun is reflected by the rocky Moon, which makes the Moon shine at night and give us moonlight.

Leap years

The Earth takes 365 and a quarter days to completely orbit the Sun. This means that every four years there are an extra four quarter days. We add the four quarters together and give that year – the leap year – an extra day. We add that day onto February, because it is the shortest of the months. In a leap year, February is 29 days long.

Some people are born on 29 February, so they will only have a birthday once every four years. They often celebrate their birthday on 28 February instead!

The seasons

The Earth is going round the Sun. The time it takes to complete a full orbit – 365 and a quarter days – we call a year.

The Earth's axis is at a slight angle to the Sun. This angle stays the same as the Earth orbits the Sun. Any point on the Earth's surface will spend some of the year leaning towards the Sun and in strong sunlight. This is summer in this part of the Earth. It will spend some of the year leaning away from the Sun, and then it will be winter in this part of the Earth.

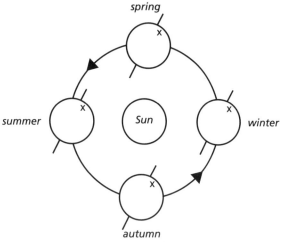

x = Great Britain

Daylight hours are longer in the summer, and shorter in the winter. Between the summer and the winter is spring, when daylight hours get longer and it gets warmer, and autumn, when daylight hours get shorter and it gets colder. On one day in the spring, and one in the autumn, day and night are exactly the same length. These days are called the equinoxes.

Daylight times

In the summer, the Sun shines early in the morning. The evenings are long and children play outside until quite late. You may even go to bed while it is still light outside. Then in the winter, daylight time is shorter. The mornings are dark and you spend the evenings indoors.

The Earth is tilted as it orbits the Sun. In the summer, the Sun appears in the sky for longer, and climbs higher. In the winter, the Sun appears in the sky for a shorter time, and does not climb so high. The changes in daylight time follow a pattern, and it is possible to predict this pattern to the minute.

Here are some sunrise and sunset times for London in the month of June 2000. The sunrise times are the time to the minute that the Sun rose. So on 8 June 2000, the Sun rose at 4.44 am – nearly a quarter to five in the morning. The sunset times are the times the Sun set. So on 8 June 2000, the Sun set at 20.14 (8.14 pm), or nearly a quarter past eight at night.

Date	Sunrise	Sunset
1st	04:48	20:08
8th	04:44	20:14
15th	04:42	20:19
22nd	04:43	20:21
29th	04:47	20:20

You can find the sunrise and sunset times on the Internet. www.onlineweather.com/v4/uk/sun/index.html has times for seven UK cities: Belfast, Birmingham, Bristol, Glasgow, London, Manchester and Newcastle.

Fascinating facts

- Eratosthenes hired a man to pace out the distance from Syene to Alexandria. He found that they were 800km apart. Eratosthenes calculated that it was 40,000km round the Earth. He was almost exactly right.

- 2,300 years ago, maps of the world showed the Mediterranean Sea in the middle of a flat Earth. People believed that if you sailed far out into the ocean, you would fall off the edge of the Earth.

Our Moon

The Moon is our satellite. Many planets have moons. Some have more than one. The Earth has one Moon – big for such a small planet. The Earth and Moon make a sort of double planet system. The Moon is about one-eightieth of the mass of the Earth. It is rotating on its axis, and orbiting the Earth. Because it takes the same time to rotate as it does to orbit, one side always faces the Earth. This time is about 27 days, about a month. As the Moon orbits the Earth, the Moon's gravity pulls on the sea, giving us the tides.

We know that the Moon's surface is rocky and powdery. There is no atmosphere, so there is no weather on the Moon. The astronauts' footprints on the Moon will never disappear. We used to think that there was no water on the Moon. But it seems possible that there is frozen water near one pole.

Why does the Moon seem to change shape?

Children may believe that:

- The Earth casts its shadow on the Moon, so it looks a different shape.
- Clouds are covering part of the Moon.
- The shadow of the Sun falls on the Moon.
- Planets cast their shadow on the Moon.

When we watch the Moon over a month, we see it appear to change in shape. These changes are called the Moon's phases. The Moon has no light of its own. It reflects the light of the Sun, even at night when the Sun is not in the sky. The shadow cast by the Sun means that the Moon appears to change in shape.

The series of pictures below show how the shadow cast by the Sun on the Moon makes those changes. The Earth is seen from below.

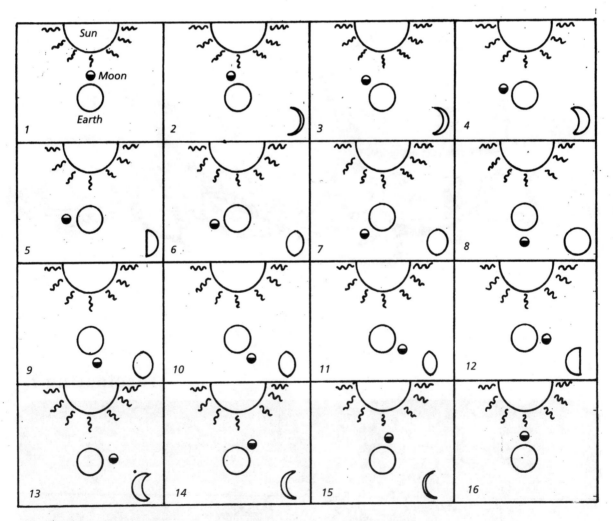

Run your eyes quickly through the pictures. They will show you how the relative positions of the Sun, Earth and Moon result in the Moon's phases.

The Sun

On Wednesday 11 August 1999, a total eclipse of the Sun was visible from much of Cornwall, parts of Devon, the Scilly Isles and Alderney. At 11.11 am, the black disc of the Moon fitted exactly over the Sun and the sky was as dark as a moonlit night.

The Sun and the Moon appear to be the same size in the sky. The Sun is much further away, so although it is much bigger than the Moon, both look the same size. And in the same way that you can cover a distant mountain with your thumbnail, so – rarely – the Moon covers the Sun, blotting it out completely. This is called an eclipse of the Sun.

Planets in the solar system

There are nine known planets orbiting the Sun. They are, in order from the Sun outwards:

- Mercury
- Venus
- Earth
- Mars
- Jupiter
- Saturn
- Uranus
- Neptune
- Pluto

Sometimes, the orbit of Pluto (which scientists now say may not be a planet in the true sense of the word) brings it inside the orbit of Neptune, closer to the Sun. Together, these planets make the solar system. The planets vary greatly in size – and they aren't as close together as shown below!

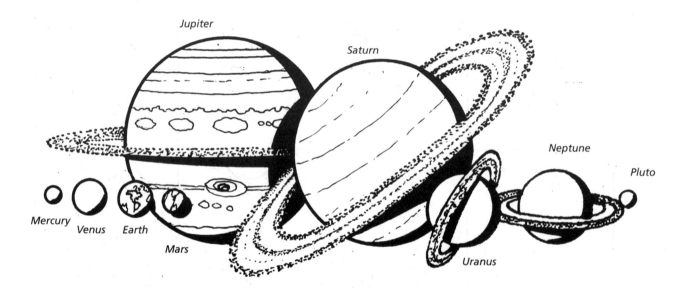

Jupiter

Saturn

Neptune

Pluto

Mercury

Venus

Earth

Mars

Uranus

Fascinating facts

- It is more than 6,000 years since the ancient Egyptians noticed that there was a regular pattern to the movement of the stars. This pattern repeated itself every 365 days. They called this period a year, and divided the year into twelve months, each of 30 days. Whoops! Five days left over. They decided to spend those five days having a great big party, starting on the day that the Dog Star rose in line with the Sun.

- Any object that orbits a planet is called a satellite. So the Moon is a satellite of the Earth. But we make satellites and launch them; and they are called artificial satellites. An artificial satellite at the right distance from Earth rotates with the planet, and can be used for telephone calls and television programmes.

Sizes and distances

The planets vary greatly in size. Jupiter, the biggest, is 143,000km across at the equator; Pluto, the smallest, is only 2,000km across. If you model the planets using fruit, then Jupiter could be a water melon and Pluto a blackcurrant, while Earth would be about the size of a strawberry.

The distances between the planets are enormous. If your home was your model of the Sun and you set off with your planet fruits, you would have to carry them away down the road to model the distances. The Pluto blackcurrant might not even be in your town! Mercury orbits the Sun every 88 Earth days, but Pluto takes 248 Earth years to make a complete orbit.

It is even further to the nearest star (after our Sun). If the Earth were a football, the next star would be in Canada.

Some planets are very hot – it is 465°C on Venus. Some are very cold – it is –220°C on Pluto.

Many moons

Earth is not the only planet with a moon. Mars has two moons – Phobos and Deimos. Jupiter has at least 16 moons, including Io and Europa. Saturn has about 23 moons, Uranus has 15 and Neptune has 8.

Space on the web

You can find out more about a whole range of space facts on the Internet. A good portal is through the Ambleside Primary School site:
www.ambleside.schoolzone.co.uk

From there you can find links to other sites, including:
www.bbc.co.uk/planets/
www.solarviews.com/eng/homepage.htm
www.ex.ac.uk/Mirrors/nineplanets
www.stsci.edu/top.html

Fascinating facts

- A red giant is a large bright star coming towards the end of its life.

- A white dwarf is a small, hot star – the last stage in the life of a star like our Sun.

- A black hole is an object in space whose gravity is so great that nothing can escape from it, not even light. Scientists believe that black holes form when a star shrinks at the end of its life. The first black hole to be found was Cygnus X-1 in 1971.

- Comets have an icy head and a tail of dust and gas. They don't trail their tail behind them. In fact, the tail may go first.

- Because the planets are so small and so far away, we don't know if there are more planets than nine. Scientists claim to have spotted other planets, but nobody is certain. There are planets round other suns in the universe. Every star could have its own solar system.

- Asteroids are pieces of rubble. There is a belt of asteroid rubble between Mars and Jupiter.

- Meteors are stony objects, some as small as a grain of sand. When they burn up in the Earth's atmosphere, we call them shooting stars. Meteorites are larger. Some crash through the atmosphere and hit the Earth.

- From the Earth, quasars appear as bright as a candle on the Moon. Astronomers need to multiply their light ten million times to study them. If a telescope collected the energy from a quasar for 10,000 years, it would be enough to light a torch bulb for a fraction of a second.

- Quasars are the most distant objects we know in the universe. They give out more energy than 100 giant galaxies.

Activities

Level One

Help the children to make routine (and safe) observations of the Sun and Moon – for example, they could record changes in the day – the apparent movement of the Sun, the change in length of shadows, the lightness of the sky.

Level Two

Invite the children to use a shadow stick to make accurate records of the change in length and direction of the shadow. Ask them to predict the length and direction of the shadow early in the morning and later in the afternoon.

Ask the children to record their results as block graphs.

Level Three

Challenge the children to model the comparative sizes and distances of the Earth, Sun and Moon using seeds, fruit or balls. Remind them to be aware of the differences in size, the huge distances involved and the relative movements.

Then challenge the children to increase their models to include the rest of the solar system. If they are using fruit, they will need a long corridor or the playground to set up their model to scale.

Level Four

Ask the children to model the day – by showing how the Earth rotates; the year – by demonstrating the orbit of the Earth around the Sun; and perhaps the month – by demonstrating the movement of the Moon around the Earth.

Invite the children to make posters to explain the day, month and year to younger children.

Level Five

Ask the children to use a globe – with its slight angle – to demonstrate how this angle results in the seasons by facing our Earth towards and away from the Sun.

Invite the children to write a letter to a friend in Australia explaining why it is winter for them when it is summer for us.

Note: Children should never look directly at the Sun. On very rare occasions, permanent damage can be done to the retina, without immediate pain.

cience is a popular, interesting and good

ubject.